Popular Complete Smart Series

Complete Canadian Curriculum

Grade

6

Contents Grade 6

Mathematics

English

Social Studies

Science

MATHEMATICS

* The Canadian penny is no longer in circulation. It is used in the units to show money amounts to the cent.

Numbers to 1 000 000 (1)

- Write, compare, and order whole numbers up to 1 000 000.
- Write numbers in expanded form and in words.
- Identify the value of a digit in a 6-digit number.

> I have a chance to win five hundred thousand dollars.

Find the least expensive house in each zone. Write the price on the line. Then answer the questions.

① The least expensive house in

Zone 1: _____

Zone 2: _____

Zone 3: _____

Zone 4: _____

Zone 1
$448 865
$339 700
$443 400

Zone 2
$674 900
$562 900
$556 680
$463 400

Zone 3
$328 400
$334 760

Hwy 416

$337 480 $439 800

School

Zone 4
$457 300
$560 280
$459 000

② Put the houses in each zone in order from the most expensive to the least expensive.

Zone 1: _____

Zone 2: _____

Zone 3: _____

Zone 4: _____

③ Which house is the most expensive among these 4 zones? In which zone is the house?

_____

④ Which house is the least expensive among these 4 zones? In which zone is it?

_____

⑤ Mr. Smith wants to buy a house near a lake and his budget is under $650 000. Which zones should he consider? Which houses should he consider in each zone?

_____

_____

⑥

> I want to buy a house near Hwy. 416 and close to a school. My budget is between $380 000 and $580 000. Which zones should I consider? Which houses should I consider in each zone?

_____

_____

⑦ If each house in Zone 3 is reduced by $1000, what will be the new price?

Old price	
New price	

⑧ If each house in Zone 4 is increased by $10 000, what will be the new price?

Old price	
New price	

6-digit Numbers:

One hundred forty-six thousand five hundred thirty-eight

Standard form
146 538

Expanded form:
100 000 + 40 000 + 6000 + 500 + 30 + 8

Write each number in expanded form, in words, or in standard form.

⑨   345 786 = _____

⑩   675 809 = _____

⑪   901 843   In words: _____

⑫   263 481   In words: _____

⑬

= 400 000 + 50 000 + 6000 + 100 + 50

= 600 000 + 3000 + 40 + 8

= 700 000 + 20 000 + 200 + 10 + 4

= 200 000 + 90 000 + 6000 + 500 + 7

Write the information in numerals.

⑭

Many people donated to the food bank last week. Three hundred six thousand one hundred sixty-five cans of food and four hundred thirty thousand ninety-four packs of crackers were collected. In addition, one hundred thousand seventy-one household items were collected.

a. _____   b. _____   c. _____

M A T H E M A T I C S

Place Value Chart:

452 986

4 is in the hundred thousand place; it means 400 000.

Thousand					
Hundred	Ten	One	Hundred	Ten	One
4	5	2	9	8	6

Look at the number for each skirt. Write the meaning of each digit. Then answer the questions.

⑮

  A 364 259

3 means _____ .

6 means _____ .

4 means _____ .

2 means _____ .

5 means _____ .

9 means _____ .

  B 461 573

4 means _____ .

6 means _____ .

1 means _____ .

5 means _____ .

7 means _____ .

3 means _____ .

  C 721 398

7 means _____ .

2 means _____ .

1 means _____ .

3 means _____ .

9 means _____ .

8 means _____ .

⑯ Which skirt has a number with

    a. a 5 in its hundreds place? _____

    b. a 9 in its tens place? _____

    c. a 2 in its ten thousands place? _____

Use the digits on the rings to form 6-digit numbers. Write them on the lines.

⑰ _____

    _____

    _____

Numbers to 1 000 000 (2)

- Locate numbers on number lines.
- Follow patterns to find missing numbers.
- Round 6-digit numbers.
- Solve problems involving large numbers.

I'll have four hundred thousand bones in June.

I don't think so.

Teddy's Bones

JAN	4
FEB	40
MAR	400
APR	4000
MAY	40 000
JUN	400 000

Use arrows to locate the numbers on the number lines.

① 136 500   138 000   140 800   135 800   143 600

136 500
↓

135 000   140 000   145 000

② 472 723   486 599   440 867   451 684   426 814

400 000   450 000   500 000

Write the value for each number on the number line.

③

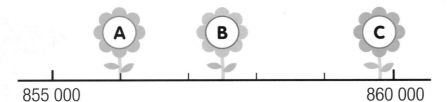

A
B
C

855 000   860 000

A _____

B _____

C _____

④

P   Q   R

600 000   700 000

P _____

Q _____

R _____

Fill in the missing numbers.

⑤ 391 111   395 555

392 222   398 888

⑥ 722 222
272 222

222 272

⑦ 475 000   790 000
480 000   680 000

495 000

Write the numbers.

⑧ a number 40 000 more than 168 453 _____

⑨ a number 200 000 less than 765 089 _____

⑩ *How many numbers are there between 892 695 and 892 703? What are they?*

_____ ; _____

_____

⑪ *How many even numbers are there between 100 927 and 100 937? What are they?*

_____ ; _____

_____

Round to the nearest hundred thousand:

1st Look at the digit in the ten thousands place.

2nd If it is 5 or greater, round the number up; otherwise, round the number down.

e.g. Round 369 751 to the nearest hundred thousand.

3 69 751

6 > 5, round the number up.

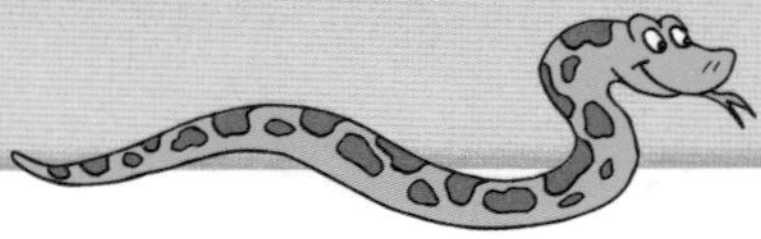

The answer is **400 000** .

See how many paper clips there are in each box. Round each number to the nearest hundred thousand. Then answer the questions.

⑫

A 405 394 _____

B 519 643 _____

C 334 965 _____

D 586 439 _____

E 608 764 _____

F 783 464 _____

⑬ Which two boxes have about the same number of paper clips? _____

⑭ Which box has the most? _____

Round each number to the nearest hundred thousand and ten thousand.

⑮ 539 642

_____ _____

⑯ 674 913

_____ _____

⑰ 802 178

_____ _____

⑱ 381 510

_____ _____

⑲ 411 063

_____ _____

⑳ 754 663

_____ _____

Solve the problems with the help of the clues. Show your work.

㉑
I drink 10 L of water a day. How many days will it take me to finish 1 000 000 L of water?

Think
1 day – 10 L
10 days – 100 L
100 days – 1000 L

_____

㉒
Uncle Ben's restaurant sells 5000 hamburgers in a month. How long will it take to sell 1 000 000 hamburgers?

Think
5000 hamburgers – 1 month
50 000 hamburgers – 10 months
500 000 hamburgers – 100 months

_____

㉓
Each elephant weighs about 4000 kg. How many elephants will have a total weight of 1 000 000 kg?

Think
4000 kg – 1 elephant
40 000 kg – 10 elephants
400 000 kg – 100 elephants

_____

㉔
A treat weighs 20 g. How many treats will have a total weight of 1 000 000 g?

_____

Multiples and Factors

This cake can be shared equally by 1, 2, 3, 6, 9, or 18 people.

- Use addition or multiplication to find the multiples of a number.
- Use multiplication to find the factors of a number.

The factors of 18 are:
1, 2, 3, 6, 9, and 18

Use addition to find the first six multiples of each number.

① 9 **+9** ⟶ _____ **+9** ⟶ _____ **+9** ⟶ _____ **+9** ⟶ _____ **+9** ⟶ _____

The first six multiples of 9: _____

② 7 **+7** ⟶ _____ **+7** ⟶ _____ **+7** ⟶ _____ **+7** ⟶ _____ **+7** ⟶ _____

The first six multiples of 7: _____

③ 12 **+12** ⟶ _____ **+12** ⟶ _____ **+12** ⟶ _____ **+12** ⟶ _____ **+12** ⟶ _____

The first six multiples of 12: _____

Find the first ten multiples of each number.

④ **The first ten multiples of**

8: _____

2: _____

5: _____

11: _____

Multiples:

products of a given whole number multiplied by other whole numbers

We can use addition or multiplication to find the multiples of a given number.

Use multiplication to find multiples:

e.g. Multiples of 4:

__4__ __8__ __12__ __16__

The first four multiples of 4: 4, 8, 12, 16

Use multiplication to find the first six multiples of each number.

⑤

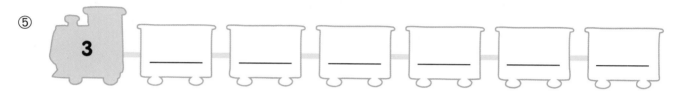

3

The first six multiples of 3: _____

⑥ **6:** _____ _____ _____ _____ _____ _____

The first six multiples of 6: _____

⑦ **10:** _____ _____ _____ _____ _____ _____

The first six multiples of 10: _____

Circle the numbers that are the multiples of the number in bold.

⑧

11 15 22 54 66 39 77

⑨

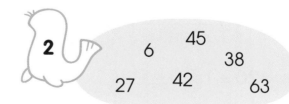

2 6 45 38 27 42 63

⑩

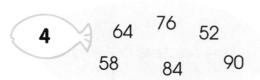

4 64 76 52 58 84 90

⑪

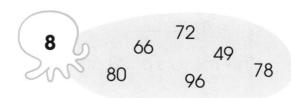

8 66 72 49 80 96 78

Factors:

whole numbers that are multiplied to get a product

To find all the factors of a number, you can think of all the multiplication facts with that number as the product.

e.g. Find the factors of 12.

$12 = 1 \times 12$
$ = 2 \times 6$
$ = 3 \times 4$
$ = 4 \times 3$ ← Stop when you get a number you've already come across.

The factors of 12 are 1, 2, 3, 4, 6, and 12.

Fill in the missing number in each multiplication sentence. Then find the factors of each number.

⑫ **10** = 1 x _____

 = 2 x _____

The factors of 10 are:

_____

⑬ **15** = 1 x _____

 = 3 x _____

The factors of 15 are:

_____

⑭ **18** = 1 x _____

 = 2 x _____

 = 3 x _____

The factors of 18 are:

_____

⑮ **24** = 1 x _____

 = 2 x _____

 = 3 x _____

 = 4 x _____

The factors of 24 are:

_____

⑯ **20** = 1 x _____

 = 2 x _____

 = 4 x _____

The factors of 20 are:

_____

⑰ **27** = 1 x _____

 = 3 x _____

The factors of 27 are:

_____

Find the factors of each number. Show your work.

⑱

9 =

16 =

17 =

28 =

30 =

	Factors
9	
16	
17	
28	
30	

Read each sentence. Put a check mark in the circle if it is correct; otherwise, put a cross and correct the underlined words or numbers.

⑲ The <u>multiples</u> of 36 are 1, 2, 3, 4, 6, 9, 12, 18, and 36.

 ; _____

⑳ <u>1</u> is a factor of all numbers.

 ; _____

㉑ The factors of 9 are 1, 3, and <u>6</u>.

 ; _____

㉒ The first four multiples of the number on my hat are <u>24, 36, 48, and 60</u>.

 ; _____

Prime Numbers and Composite Numbers

- Identify prime numbers and composite numbers.
- Use factor trees to write numbers as products of prime factors.
- Understand the relationship between prime numbers and composite numbers.

Composite numbers

$42 = 2 \times 3 \times 7$
$54 = 2 \times 3 \times 3 \times 3$

Fill in the blanks with the given words or numbers.

①

1
5
20
Composite
Prime

- _____ number: any number greater than 1 that has more than 2 factors

  e.g. _____ is a composite number.

- _____ number: any number with only 1 and itself as factors

  e.g. _____ is a prime number.

* _____ is neither a composite number nor a prime number.

Write the factors of each number. Then write "prime" or "composite" to complete each sentence.

② **16:** _____

16 is a _____ number.

③ **7:** _____

7 is a _____ number.

④ **12:** _____

12 is a _____ number.

⑤ **18:** _____

18 is a _____ number.

Cross out or colour the numbers on the 100-chart. Then answer the questions and fill in the blanks.

⑥

Put a cross on number 1. Then colour the composite numbers orange.

1	2	3	4	5	6	7	8	9	10
11	12	13	14	15	16	17	18	19	20
21	22	23	24	25	26	27	28	29	30
31	32	33	34	35	36	37	38	39	40
41	42	43	44	45	46	47	48	49	50
51	52	53	54	55	56	57	58	59	60
61	62	63	64	65	66	67	68	69	70
71	72	73	74	75	76	77	78	79	80
81	82	83	84	85	86	87	88	89	90
91	92	93	94	95	96	97	98	99	100

⑦ How many prime numbers are there between 1 and 100? What are they?

_____

_____

⑧ How many composite numbers are there between 1 and 53? What are they?

_____

_____

⑨ _____ is the only prime number that is an even number.

⑩ All even numbers, except 2, are _____ (prime/composite) numbers.

⑪

The smallest prime number is _____ .

4

Steps to write a number as a product of prime factors:

1st Write the composite number as the product of two factors.

2nd Continue to factorize each composite number until all factors are prime numbers.

3rd Write the number as a product of prime factors.

e.g.

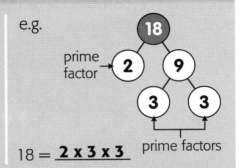

prime factor →

$18 = \underline{\textbf{2 x 3 x 3}}$ prime factors

Write each number as a product of prime factors. Show your work.

⑫

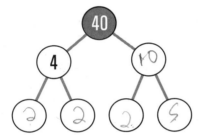

$40 = \underline{\quad} \times \underline{\quad} \times \underline{\quad} \times \underline{\quad}$

⑬

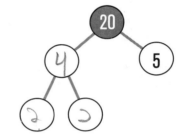

$20 = \underline{\quad} \times \underline{\quad} \times \underline{\quad}$

⑭

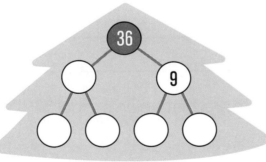

$36 = \underline{\quad} \times \underline{\quad} \times \underline{\quad} \times \underline{\quad}$

⑮

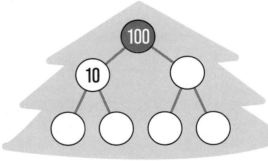

$100 = \underline{\quad} \times \underline{\quad} \times \underline{\quad} \times \underline{\quad}$

⑯

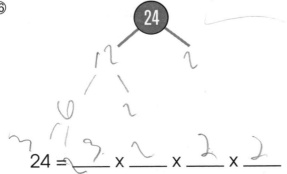

$24 = \underline{\quad} \times \underline{\quad} \times \underline{\quad} \times \underline{\quad}$

⑰

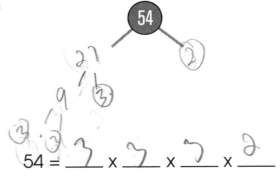

$54 = \underline{\quad} \times \underline{\quad} \times \underline{\quad} \times \underline{\quad}$

Match each number with its product of prime factors.

⑱

64 •

105 •

36 •

90 •

75 •

• 3 x 5 x 7

• 2 x 3 x 3 x 5

• 2 x 2 x 2 x 2 x 2 x 2

• 2 x 2 x 3 x 3

• 3 x 5 x 5

Write each number as a product of prime factors.

⑲ 38 = _2_ x _19_

⑳ 50 = ___ x ___ x ___

㉑ 28 = _2_ x _2_ x _7_

㉒ 45 = ___ x ___ x ___

㉓ 52 = _2_ x _2_ x _13_

㉔ 60 = ___ x ___ x ___ x ___

㉕ 10 = _2 x 5_

㉖ 81 = _____

㉗ 56 = _____

㉘ 90 = _____

㉙ 91 = _____

㉚ 14 = _____

Read what the girl says. Answer her questions.

㉛ *Can any composite number be factored into prime factors?*

_____

㉜ *The greater the number is, the more prime factors it has.   Am I correct?*

_____

Addition and Subtraction of Whole Numbers

- Add and subtract whole numbers.
- Estimate and check answers.
- Do mixed operations with or without brackets.
- Solve problems involving mixed operations.

Total No. of Points

$$
\begin{array}{r}
\overset{1}{3}\,4\,\overset{1}{6}\,2\,7 \\
+\;1\,8\,1\,2\,5 \\
\hline
5\,2\,7\,5\,2
\end{array}
$$

Do you know that the total number of points we got in Games A and B is 52 752?

The answer to each question shows the number of pennies that each class collected for charity. Calculate. Then answer the questions.

①

Mr. Smith's class

$$
\begin{array}{r}
3\,4\,1\,0\,3 \\
+\quad 8\,5\,4\,2 \\
\hline
\end{array}
$$

Mrs. Winter's class

$$
\begin{array}{r}
5\,0\,0\,6\,3 \\
-\quad 7\,4\,5\,9 \\
\hline
\end{array}
$$

Mrs. Gault's class

$$
\begin{array}{r}
2\,7\,6\,5\,4 \\
+\;1\,8\,3\,4\,9 \\
\hline
\end{array}
$$

Ms. LeBlanc's class

74 653 – 40 198 = _____

Ms. Dottori's class

38 759 + 4666 = _____

Mr. Wood's class

53 625 – 17 908 = _____

Mrs. McLellan's class

8459 + 27 776 = _____

Ms. Carter's class

70 284 – 11 789 = _____

Mrs. Goldberger's class

538 + 16 589 = _____

② How much did Ms. Carter's class collect in dollars? _____

③ Which class collected the most? _____

④ How many classes collected more than $400? _____

Estimate by rounding each number to the nearest thousand. Then find the exact answer.

Number of Boxes of Juice Sold

Yesterday: 46 382 boxes

Today: 82 146 boxes

Number of Balloons

Red: 46 583

Yellow: 43 177

⑤ How many boxes of juice were sold in these two days?

- About _____ boxes

- _____ boxes

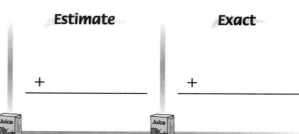

Estimate

$+$ _____

Exact

$+$ _____

⑥ How many more boxes of juice were sold today than yesterday?

- About _____ boxes more

- _____ boxes more

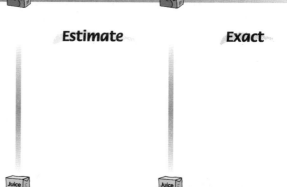

Estimate

Exact

⑦ How many balloons are there in all?

- About _____ balloons

- _____ balloons

Estimate

Exact

⑧ How many more red balloons than yellow balloons are there?

- About _____ balloons more

- _____ balloons more

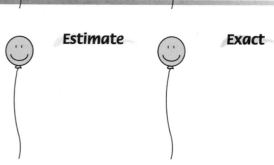

Estimate

Exact

Solving problems without brackets:

853 − 464 + 131 ← Follow the order of operations (from left to right) to find the answer.

= 389 + 131

= **520**

Solving problems with brackets:

853 − (464 + 131) ← Do the part inside the brackets first.

= 853 − 595

= **258**

Find the answers.

⑨ 679 + 186 − 254

= _____

= _____

⑩ 365 − 27 + 182

= _____

= _____

⑪ 723 − (144 + 96)

= _____

= _____

⑫ 386 + (279 − 58)

= _____

= _____

⑬ (842 + 79) − 63

= _____

= _____

⑭ 466 − 123 + 97

= _____

= _____

⑮ 973 + 149 − 68 = _____

⑯ 5000 − 273 + 362 = _____

⑰ 524 + (226 − 72) = _____

⑱ (439 + 439) − 358 = _____

Put "+" or "−" in the spaces provided to complete the number sentences.

⑲ 376 ◯ 196 ◯ 654 = *834*

⑳ 717 ◯ 263 ◯ 218 = *236*

㉑ 582 ◯ 615 ◯ 523 = *674*

Help the children solve the problems.

㉒ Judy got 27 546 points and 34 668 points in the first two rounds of a game. How many points did Judy get in all?

_____ = _____   _____

㉓ Katie got 50 864 points at first, but she had a penalty of 476 points. How many points did Katie get in the end?

_____ = _____   _____

㉔ Kevin got 7642 points and Ron got 827 fewer points. How many points did Kevin and Ron get in all?

_____ = _____   _____

㉕ Mandy had got 9476 points. After she was trapped twice and lost 475 points each time, how many points did she get in the end?

_____ = _____   _____

㉖ If Wilson got 255 points more, he would have 8000 points. How many points did Wilson actually get?

_____ = _____   _____

㉗

> *I'll have thirty thousand points if I get 5 more points.*
> *How many points have I got?*

_____ = _____

_____

Multiplication of Whole Numbers

- Multiply 2-digit numbers and 3-digit numbers by 2-digit numbers.
- Use the commutative property of multiplication to find answers in a faster way.
- Solve problems involving multiplication.

I can go 320 m in 1 min.

$$\begin{array}{r} 3\,2\,0 \\ \times\quad 1\,5 \\ \hline 1\,6\,0\,0 \\ 3\,2\,0\,0 \\ \hline 4\,8\,0\,0 \end{array}$$

You can go 4800 m in 15 min.

Do the multiplication.

①
$$\begin{array}{r} 5\,8 \\ \times\quad 2\,9 \\ \hline \end{array}$$

②
$$\begin{array}{r} 6\,3 \\ \times\quad 4\,7 \\ \hline \end{array}$$

③
$$\begin{array}{r} 3\,2 \\ \times\quad 8\,9 \\ \hline \end{array}$$

④ 74 x 64 = _____

⑤ 53 x 37 = _____

⑥ 43 x 43 = _____

⑦ 29 x 16 = _____

⑧ 52 x 61 = _____

⑨ 34 x 78 = _____

⑩ 83 x 24 = _____

⑪ 35 x 11 = _____

⑫ 49 x 26 = _____

⑬ 64 x 57 = _____

Fill in the missing numbers.

⑭
$$\begin{array}{r} 2\,\text{✿} \\ \times\quad \text{✿}\,5 \\ \hline 1\,3\,0 \\ 5\,2\,\text{✿} \\ \hline \text{✿}\,\text{✿}\,0 \end{array}$$

⑮
$$\begin{array}{r} \text{🌷}\,3 \\ \times\quad 4\,\text{🌷} \\ \hline 1\,6\,1 \\ 9\,\text{🌷}\,\text{🌷} \\ \hline \text{🌷}\,\text{🌷}\,8\,1 \end{array}$$

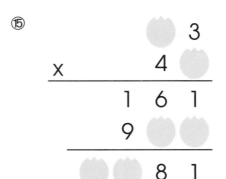

A 3-digit number x A 2-digit number:

1st Multiply the ones.

2nd Multiply the tens.

3rd Add the products from **1st** and **2nd** steps.

Multiply the ones.	Multiply the tens.	Add.

```
    4 2 5          4 2 5          4 2 5
 x    3 9       x    3 9       x    3 9
 ---------      ---------      ---------
    3 8 2 5        3 8 2 5        3 8 2 5
                1 2 7 5 0      1 2 7 5 0
                               ---------
                               1 6 5 7 5
```

425 x 39 = __16 575__

Do the multiplication.

⑯
```
      1 2 9
 x      5 4
```

⑰
```
      4 9 6
 x      6 7
```

⑱
```
      5 2 3
 x      8 9
```

⑲ 276 x 18 = _____

⑳ 359 x 47 = _____

㉑ 814 x 63 = _____

㉒ 416 x 84 = _____

㉓ 117 x 35 = _____

㉔ 209 x 56 = _____

Find the total number of candies.

㉕

Total number of candies	
12 jars	candies
37 jars	
43 jars	

㉖

Total number of candies	
15 boxes	candies
24 boxes	
42 boxes	

Commutative Property:

In multiplication, numbers can be multiplied in any order.

e.g. 4 x 16 x 5 = 4 x 5 x 16 ⟵ Multiply 4 and 5 first to get a number which is a multiple of 10.

$\qquad$ = 20 x 16

$\qquad$ = 320

You can multiply the numbers in any order. The easiest way is to multiply the numbers with a product that is a multiple of 10, 100, or 1000 first.

Use the commutative property to do the multiplication.

㉗ 8 x 27 x 5

= _____ x _____ x 27

= _____ x 27

= _____

㉘ 35 x 9 x 2

= _____

= _____

= _____

㉙ 23 x 6 x 5

= _____

= _____

= _____

㉚ 18 x 9 x 5

= _____

= _____

= _____

㉛ 63 x 14 x 5

= _____

= _____

= _____

㉜ 75 x 19 x 4

= _____

= _____

= _____

Find the totals. Show your work.

㉝   Each bead weighs 15 g.
A box has 6 sections.
Each section has 88 beads.

Total weight of the beads:

㉞  Each row has 9 boxes of juice.
There are 6 rows in a case.
Each box holds 145 mL of juice.

Total amount of juice:

Solve the problems. Show your work.

Should I buy 15 tins or 138 boxes of crackers so that I can have more crackers?

Mrs. Green

Mrs. Green should buy _____ .

Which hold more cookies, 25 big boxes or 38 small boxes?

_____ hold more cookies.

Mr. Russell has prepared 36 boxes and 14 bottles of juice for us. How much juice do we have in all?

We have _____ of juice in all.

Division of Whole Numbers

- Divide 3-digit numbers and 4-digit numbers by 2-digit numbers.
- Use the distributive property to find answers in a faster way.
- Solve problems involving division.

```
        3 8 8
12 ) 4 6 5 6
      3 6
      1 0 5
        9 6
          9 6
          9 6
```

4656 balls for 12 ball pits

Derek, can you believe that we are playing with 388 balls?

Do the division.

①
$$34) \overline{4 6 7}$$ R

②
$$69) \overline{5 7 2}$$

③
$$14) \overline{9 8 1}$$

④ $414 \div 23 =$ _____

⑤ $503 \div 28 =$ _____

⑥ $357 \div 18 =$ _____

⑦ $835 \div 46 =$ _____

⑧ $582 \div 79 =$ _____

⑨ $463 \div 37 =$ _____

⑩ $254 \div 65 =$ _____

⑪ $700 \div 56 =$ _____

⑫

984 g

a. Jason cuts a cake equally into 12 slices. Each slice weighs _____ g.

b. If 18 cakes cost $432, one cake costs $ _____ .

Steps to do division:

$$86 \overline{)1174} \leftarrow \begin{array}{l} 11 < 86; \text{ consider} \\ 1 \text{ more digit} \end{array}$$

$$\begin{array}{r} 1\,3 \text{ R56} \\ 86 \overline{)1174} \\ 86 \\ \hline 314 \\ 258 \\ \hline 56 \end{array} \leftarrow \begin{array}{l} \text{There is 1 "86"} \\ \text{in 117.} \end{array}$$

$1174 \div 86 = \underline{\textbf{13R56}}$

When a 4–digit number is divided by a 2–digit number, the quotient must be a 2– or 3–digit number.

Do the division.

⑬
$$16 \overline{)3782}$$

⑭
$$39 \overline{)4018}$$

⑮
$$95 \overline{)8109}$$

⑯ 5230 ÷ 72 = _____

⑰ 5164 ÷ 46 = _____

⑱ 2713 ÷ 54 = _____

⑲ 7020 ÷ 18 = _____

⑳ 3969 ÷ 49 = _____

㉑ 4004 ÷ 33 = _____

㉒ 2586 ÷ 24 = _____

㉓ 3507 ÷ 26 = _____

㉔ There are 2312 cars in a parking lot. If there are 34 cars in a lane, how many lanes are there in the parking lot? _____

㉕ If Mr. Smith collects $1248 from 48 cars, how much does each driver pay for the parking fee on average? _____

Distributive Property:

e.g. $(500 + 15) \div 5$ ⟵ Remove brackets by dividing each term in the brackets by 5.

= $500 \div 5 + 15 \div 5$ ⟵ Do the division first.

= $100 + 3$

= **103**

You can use arrows to remind yourself to divide each term.

$(500 + 15) \div 5$

It is like a rainbow.

Use the distributive property to do the division.   Draw lines to match the questions with the correct answers.

㉖

$(400 + 40) \div 4$ •

$(250 + 55) \div 5$ •

$(800 - 72) \div 8$ •

$(770 - 7) \div 7$ •

$(66 + 42) \div 6$ •

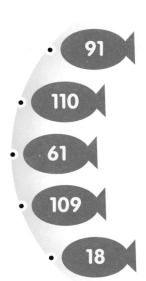

• 91

• 110

• 61

• 109

• 18

Use the distributive property to do the division. Show your work.

㉗ $(330 + 45) \div 3$

= _____

= _____

= _____

㉘ $(360 - 81) \div 9$

= _____

= _____

= _____

㉙ $(714 - 49) \div 7 =$ _____

㉚ $(800 - 36) \div 4 =$ _____

㉛ $(280 + 84) \div 2 =$ _____

㉜ $(450 + 55) \div 5 =$ _____

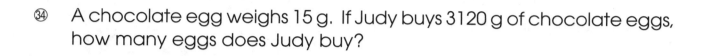
Solve the problems.

㉝ Mrs. Cowan has a bag of soil weighing 8240 g. If she puts the soil equally into 16 flowerpots, how many grams of soil will each pot hold?

_____ = _____   _____

㉞ A chocolate egg weighs 15 g. If Judy buys 3120 g of chocolate eggs, how many eggs does Judy buy?

_____ = _____   _____

㉟

Uncle Sam buys a washing machine and pays by 12 equal instalments. How much does Uncle Sam need to pay in each instalment?

_____ = _____   _____

㊱

Area:
8448 cm²

Mandy divides a gift wrap into 24 equal pieces. What is the area of each piece?

_____ = _____   _____

㊲

Each net can hold 32 balls. How many nets are needed to hold 2000 balls?

_____ = _____   _____

㊳

There are 78 children playing in the kids zone. If Mr. Smith gives 250 pencils to the children, how many pencils will each child get? How many pencils will be left?

_____ = _____

_____ ; _____

Operations with Whole Numbers

- Do addition, subtraction, multiplication, and division with whole numbers.
- Round numbers to estimate answers.
- Understand and use different strategies to solve problems.
- Solve problems involving mixed operations.

We have 8715 g of candies.

Find the answers.

①
$$
\begin{array}{r}
4\,5\,2\,9\,3 \\
-\ 1\,8\,6\,7\,9 \\
\hline
\end{array}
$$

②
$$
\begin{array}{r}
3\,8\,1\,6\,4 \\
+\ 3\,9\,0\,8\,8 \\
\hline
\end{array}
$$

③
$$
38\,\overline{)4673}
$$

④
$$
\begin{array}{r}
3\,4\,7 \\
\times\quad 6\,8 \\
\hline
\end{array}
$$

⑤
$$
\begin{array}{r}
2\,5\,3 \\
\times\quad 1\,9 \\
\hline
\end{array}
$$

⑥ 14 655 + 8249 = _____

⑦ 411 x 27 = _____

⑧ 60 027 – 11 763 = _____

⑨ 8069 ÷ 33 = _____

⑩ 37 260 + 48 293 = _____

⑪ 664 x 12 = _____

Put "+", "–", "x", or "÷" in the circles.

⑫ 34 195 ◯ 2893 = *31 302*

⑬ 316 ◯ 16 = *5056*

⑭ 8730 ◯ 45 = *194*

⑮ 17 063 ◯ 225 = *17 288*

Round the numbers to estimate the answers. Draw lines to the best estimates.

⑯

54 293 + 27 886 •

8025 ÷ 19 •

116 x 59 •

893 x 28 •

487 x 88 •

3216 ÷ 31 •

60 274 – 49 184 •

• about 27 000

• about 10 000

• about 45 000

• about 400

• about 6000

• about 80 000

• about 100

Read what the children say. Help them estimate the answers.

⑰

I have 27 825 mL of juice. If my family drink 1524 mL of juice, we'll have about _____ mL of juice left.

A glass holds 375 mL of juice. 85 glasses hold about _____ mL of juice.

⑱

I have 12 476 pennies. If I collect 7826 more pennies, I'll have about _____ pennies in all.

I divided 4886 pennies equally into 52 groups. There are about _____ pennies in each group.

Check the correct strategies to solve the problems. Then find the answers.

⑲ Vivian has bought 18 big bags and 18 small bags of chips. How many grams of chips has she bought in all?

 **Strategy 1**
1st – Find the total weight of 18 big bags.
2nd – Find the total weight of 18 small bags.
3rd – Add the products.

 **Strategy 2**
1st – Find the difference in weight between 1 big bag and 1 small bag.
2nd – Multiply the difference by 18.

Strategy 3
1st – Find the total weight of 1 big bag and 1 small bag.
2nd – Multiply the sum by 18.

I've bought _____ g of chips in all.

⑳ Mr. White divides the red marbles into 6 equal groups and does the same with the blue marbles. Then he gives 1 group of each to Tom. How many marbles does Tom get in all?

 **Strategy 1**
1st – Find the total number of marbles.
2nd – Divide the sum by 6.

 **Strategy 2**
1st – Divide the number of blue marbles by 6.
2nd – Divide the number of red marbles by 6.
3rd – Find the sum of the quotients.

 **Strategy 3**
1st – Find the total number of marbles.
2nd – Multiply the sum by 6.

I get _____ marbles in all.

Read what the children say. Help them solve the problems with the help of the clues.

㉑

I have a box of chocolates. If I give 900 g of chocolates to my parents and share the rest equally with my 2 sisters, how many grams of chocolates do I get?

(_____ ◯ _____) ◯ _____ = _____

She gets _____ g of chocolates.

2772 g

㉒

I have 3 boxes of markers. If I put them equally into 4 boxes, how many markers are there in each box?

There are _____ markers in each box.

128 Markers

㉓

My mom puts a box of cookies equally on 7 plates and gives 1 plate to me. If I eat 2 cookies, how many cookies will be left on my plate?

_____ cookies will be left.

56 Cookies

㉔

I have a bag of candies. If I can have all the candies in the boxes too, how many grams will I have in all?

He will have _____ g of candies.

1245 g
1245 g
1245 g
1245 g
1245 g
1245 g
1245 g

608 g

Perimeter and Area (1)

- Draw squares and rectangles with given dimensions and use formulas to find the perimeters and areas.
- Draw polygons with given dimensions and find the perimeters.
- Use a formula to find the perimeters of regular polygons.
- Find the perimeters of irregular polygons.

I can use a bungee cord to make a square with a perimeter of 120 cm and an area of 900 cm².

Draw the rectangle or square and label the sides. Then use formulas to find the perimeters and areas of the shapes.

① a rectangle with length 46 mm and width 28 mm

$$\textbf{Perimeter} = 2 \times \underline{\hspace{1cm}} + 2 \times \underline{\hspace{1cm}}$$

$$= \underline{\hspace{1cm}} (\quad)$$

$$\textbf{Area} = \underline{\hspace{1cm}} \times \underline{\hspace{1cm}}$$

$$= \underline{\hspace{1cm}} (\quad)$$

② a square with side length 37 mm

$$\textbf{Perimeter} =$$

$$\textbf{Area} =$$

Draw 3 different triangles each with an area of 12 cm². Then find the perimeter of each triangle and write the answer on it.

③

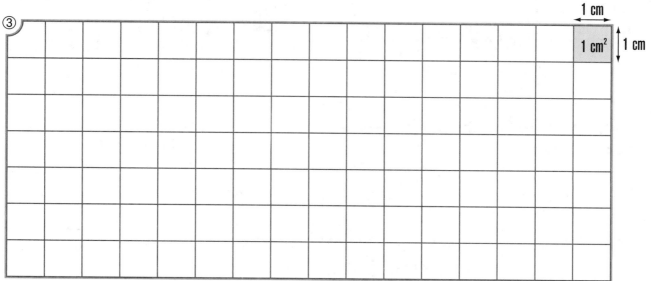

1 cm

1 cm² 1 cm

Draw a triangle with the two given sides. Then find the perimeter of the triangle.

④   sides: 25 mm, 4 cm

⑤   sides: 52 mm, 35 mm

Perimeter = _____

Perimeter = _____

⑥   sides: 6 cm, 46 mm

⑦   sides: 4 cm, 62 mm

Perimeter = _____

Perimeter = _____

Formula for finding the perimeter of a regular polygon: Perimeter = **side length x no. of sides**	**Regular hexagon** 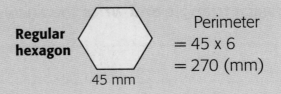 45 mm	Perimeter = 45 x 6 = 270 (mm)

Use formulas to find the perimeters of the regular polygons.

Perimeter of

⑧

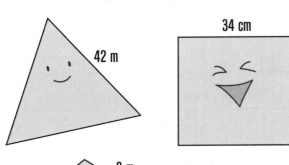

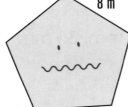

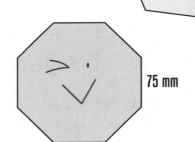

34 cm

42 m

8 m

26 cm

75 mm

triangle	= _____
	= _____ ( )
square	= _____
	= _____ ( )
pentagon	= _____
	= _____ ( )
hexagon	= _____
	= _____ ( )
octagon	= _____
	= _____ ( )

⑨ A heptagon has a side length of 16 cm. What is its perimeter?

_____ = _____   _____

⑩ A regular polygon has 14 sides. If each side is 12 mm long, what is its perimeter?

_____ = _____   _____

Find the perimeters of the irregular polygons.

⑪

A

regular hexagon

square

12 cm

B

regular octagon

regular pentagon

8 mm

C

equilateral triangle

15 cm

7 cm

28 cm

D

18 cm

9 cm

square

square

18 cm

E

square

23 m

regular hexagon

F

42 mm

square

regular pentagon

Perimeter

A _____

B _____

C _____

D _____

E _____

F _____

⑫

equilateral triangle

6 cm

rectangle

20 cm

_____

Area = 20 x 30
= 600 (cm²)

Area = 20 x 30
= 600 (cm²)

Perimeter and Area (2)

- Find the relationships between the area of a rectangle and the areas of parallelograms and triangles.

- Use formulas to find the area of a parallelogram and a triangle.

- Solve problems related to perimeters and areas.

I think I have a bigger area!

Actually, we have the same area.

See how Jason cuts each parallelogram. Draw the rectangle formed and label the sides. Then find the area of the parallelogram.

① 9 cm

7 cm

rectangle formed

Area of the parallelogram

= Area of the rectangle

= _____ x _____

= _____ (cm²)

②

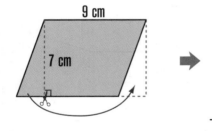

10 cm

15 cm

rectangle formed

Area of the parallelogram

= Area of the rectangle

= _____ x _____

= _____ (cm²)

③ 18 cm

6 cm

rectangle formed

Area of the parallelogram

= Area of the rectangle

= _____ x _____

= _____ (cm²)

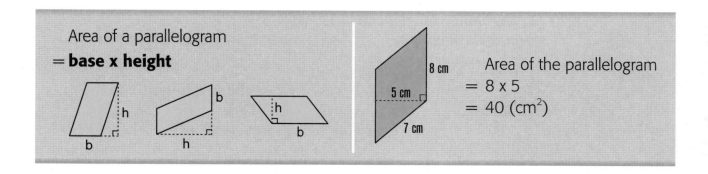

Area of a parallelogram
= **base x height**

Area of the parallelogram
= 8 x 5
= 40 (cm²)

8 cm
5 cm
7 cm

Find the areas of the parallelograms.

④

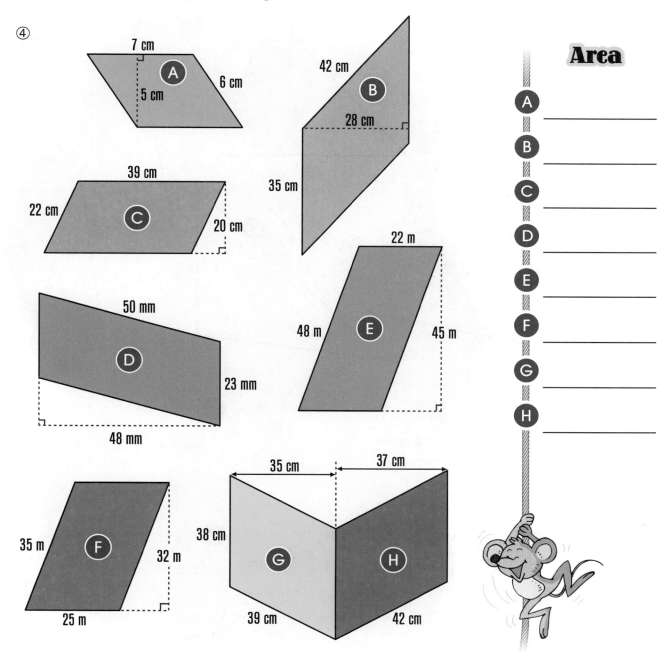

A 7 cm, 5 cm, 6 cm

B 42 cm, 28 cm, 35 cm

C 39 cm, 22 cm, 20 cm

D 50 mm, 23 mm, 48 mm

E 22 m, 48 m, 45 m

F 35 m, 32 m, 25 m

G 35 cm, 38 cm, 39 cm

H 37 cm, 42 cm

Area

A _____

B _____

C _____

D _____

E _____

F _____

G _____

H _____

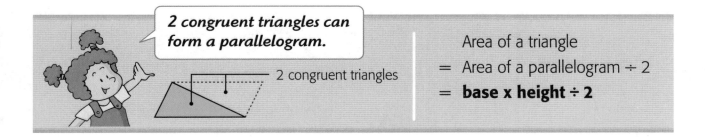

2 congruent triangles can form a parallelogram.

2 congruent triangles

Area of a triangle
= Area of a parallelogram ÷ 2
= **base x height ÷ 2**

Look at each triangle with the given base. Draw a line to show and measure the height of the triangle. Then find its area.

⑤

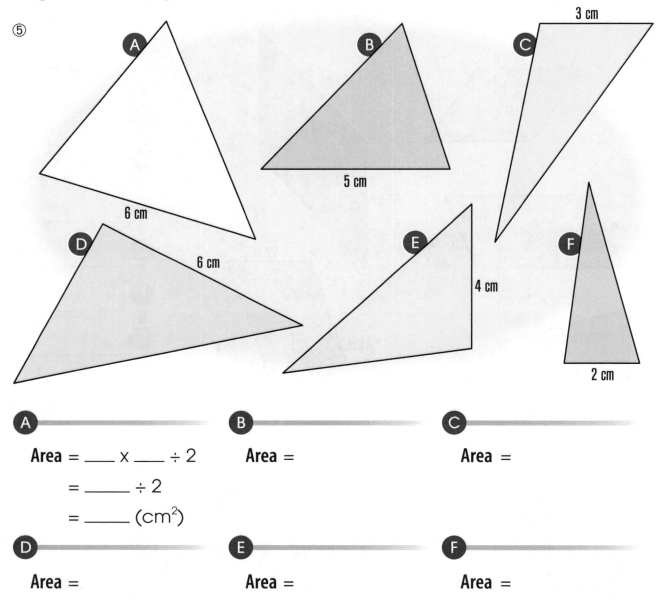

A

Area = ___ x ___ ÷ 2

= _____ ÷ 2

= _____ (cm²)

B

Area =

C

Area =

D

Area =

E

Area =

F

Area =

Solve the problems.

⑥ A rectangular cardboard is 50 cm long and 20 cm wide. If Jack cuts along the dotted lines to get a parallelogram,

a. what is the area of the parallelogram?

_____

b. what is the perimeter of the parallelogram?

_____

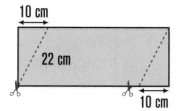

⑦ Sue has a triangular cardboard with 3 equal sides. If she cuts it into 9 identical triangles,

a. what is the area of each small triangle?

_____

b. what is the perimeter of each small triangle?

_____

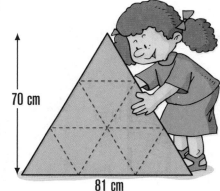

⑧ Mr. Green cuts along the dotted lines to get an equilateral triangle and a pentagon from the rectangle.

a. What is the area of the triangle?

_____

b. What is the perimeter of the pentagon?

_____

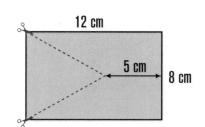

⑨

My friend, Marco, is formed by 5 congruent parallelograms. What is his area?

_____

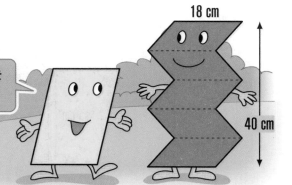

Volume and Surface Area

- Find the relationship between the height, the area of the base, and the volume of a prism.
- Use a formula to find the volume of a prism.
- Find the surface area of a rectangular or triangular prism.

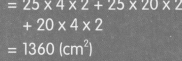

20 cm
4 cm 25 cm

The surface area of this box is 1360 cm².

See how the prisms are formed. Find the volumes of the prisms.

① by stacking 1000 bookmarks

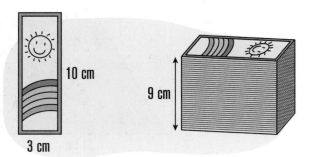

10 cm
9 cm
3 cm

Volume of a stack of bookmarks

= _____ X _____ X _____

= _____ (cm³)

② by stacking 100 coasters

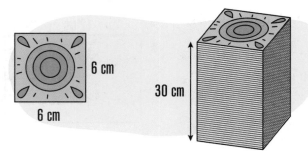

6 cm
30 cm
6 cm

Volume of a stack of coasters

= _____ X _____ X _____

= _____ (cm³)

③ by stacking 10 000 sheets of paper

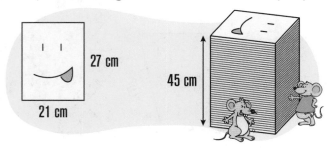

27 cm
45 cm
21 cm

Volume of a stack of paper

= _____ X _____ X _____

= _____ (cm³)

Formula for finding the volume of a prism:

Volume = **area of base x height**

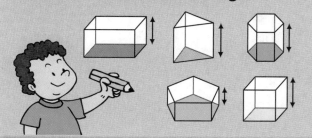

e.g.

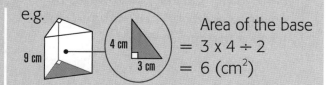

Area of the base
= 3 x 4 ÷ 2
= 6 (cm²)

Volume of the triangular prism
= 6 x 9
= 54 (cm³)

Find the area of the base of each prism. Then find the volume.

④

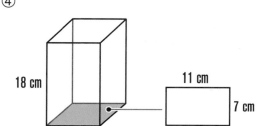

Area of the base = _____

= _____ (   )

Volume = _____

= _____ (   )

⑤

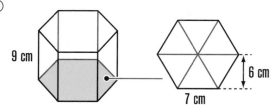

Area of the base =

Volume =

⑥

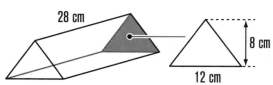

Area of the base =

Volume =

⑦

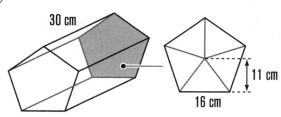

Area of the base =

Volume =

How many square centimetres of wrapping paper are needed to wrap a triangular prism?

Find the surface area of the prism.

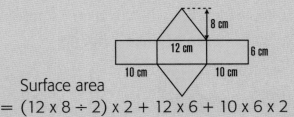

Surface area
= (12 x 8 ÷ 2) x 2 + 12 x 6 + 10 x 6 x 2
= 288

288 cm² of wrapping paper are needed.

Draw to complete the net and label the sides of each prism. Then find the surface area of the prism.

⑧

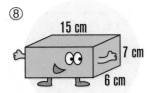

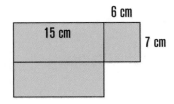

Surface area

=

⑨

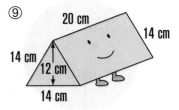

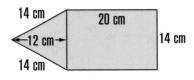

Surface area

=

Find the surface area of each prism.

⑩

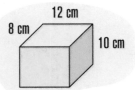

⑪

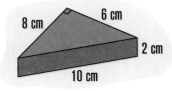

⑫

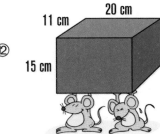

_____   _____   _____

Look at the boxes. Answer the questions.

⑬   What is the volume of (A) ?

⑭   What is the volume of (B) ?

_____

_____

⑮

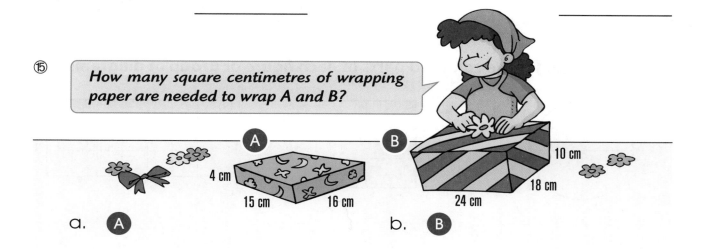

How many square centimetres of wrapping paper are needed to wrap A and B?

a. (A)

b. (B)

_____

_____

⑯

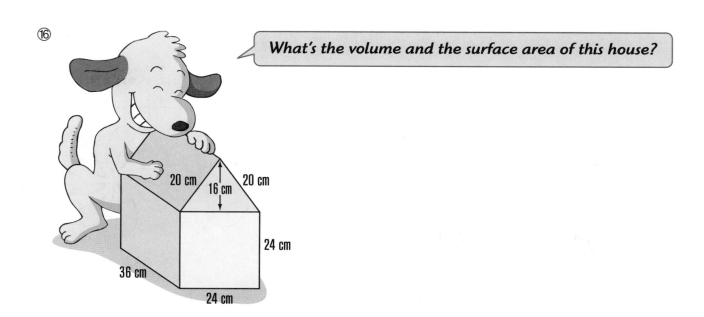

What's the volume and the surface area of this house?

Fractions

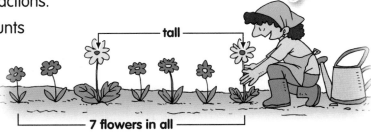

2 out of 7 flowers are tall.
$\frac{2}{7}$ of my flowers are tall.

- Identify and write different types of fractions.
- Compare and order fractional amounts with unlike denominators.
- Solve simple word problems related to fractions.

tall

7 flowers in all

Write a fraction for the coloured parts of each figure or group of diagrams.

① 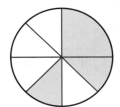 _____

② 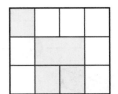 _____

③  _____

④

_____ improper fraction   _____ mixed number

⑤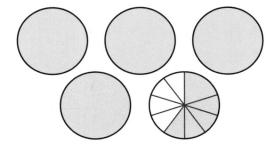

_____ improper fraction   _____ mixed number

⑥

_____ improper fraction   _____ mixed number

⑦

_____ improper fraction   _____ mixed number

Colour the parts to match the fractions. Then put "<" or ">" in the spaces provided.

⑧ $\frac{4}{5}$

$\frac{2}{3}$

$\frac{4}{5}$ ⬭ $\frac{2}{3}$

⑨ $\frac{2}{6}$

$\frac{3}{8}$

$\frac{2}{6}$ ⬭ $\frac{3}{8}$

⑩ $\frac{9}{12}$ $\frac{7}{10}$

$\frac{9}{12}$ ⬆ $\frac{7}{10}$

⑪ $\frac{3}{5}$ $\frac{5}{7}$

$\frac{3}{5}$ ⬆ $\frac{5}{7}$

Compare each pair of fractions. Draw and colour simple diagrams of your own to show the fractions. Then circle the greater one.

⑫ $\frac{9}{10}$ $\frac{5}{6}$

⑬ $\frac{4}{5}$ $\frac{2}{3}$

⑭ $\frac{1}{2}$ $\frac{5}{8}$

⑮ $\frac{3}{4}$ $\frac{6}{10}$

Steps to compare mixed numbers with different denominators:

1st Compare the whole number parts. The one with a greater number is greater. If they are the same, go to step 2.

2nd Compare the fraction parts by using diagrams. The one with a greater part is greater.

e.g. $3\frac{3}{10}$ $\quad$ $3\frac{2}{5}$

the same; compare the fraction parts

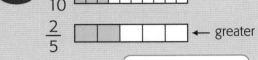

1st $3\frac{3}{10}$ $\quad$ $3\frac{2}{5}$

2nd $\frac{3}{10}$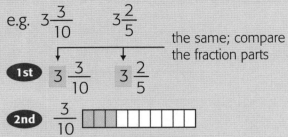

$\frac{2}{5}$ ← greater

$3\frac{2}{5}$ is greater.

Circle the greater fraction in each pair.

⑯ $2\frac{3}{7}$ $\quad$ $4\frac{9}{10}$

⑰ $3\frac{4}{5}$ $\quad$ $3\frac{1}{2}$

⑱ $7\frac{2}{3}$ $\quad$ $6\frac{8}{10}$

⑲ $4\frac{1}{2}$ $\quad$ $5\frac{2}{3}$

⑳ $1\frac{3}{10}$ $\quad$ $1\frac{1}{2}$

㉑ $2\frac{5}{6}$ $\quad$ $2\frac{2}{4}$

Draw and colour the diagrams to show the fractions. Then put them in order from greatest to least.

㉒ $1\frac{2}{3}$

$\frac{5}{4}$

$1\frac{1}{2}$

㉓ $1\frac{3}{5}$

$\frac{3}{2}$

$1\frac{1}{3}$

In order: _____

In order: _____

When fractions with different denominators have the same numerators, the one with the smallest denominator is the greatest.

e.g. $\frac{3}{10}$ $\frac{3}{4}$ $\frac{3}{9}$ ← same numerators

Consider the denominators:

$\frac{3}{10}$ $\frac{3}{4}$ $\frac{3}{9}$ ← 4 is the smallest.

$\frac{3}{4}$ is the greatest one.

Circle the greatest fraction in each group.

㉔ $\frac{5}{8}$ $\frac{5}{6}$ $\frac{5}{12}$ ㉕ $\frac{7}{9}$ $\frac{7}{18}$ $\frac{7}{16}$ ㉖ $\frac{9}{15}$ $\frac{9}{10}$ $\frac{9}{6}$

Colour the pictures to match the fractions. Then answer the question.

㉗ **Flour** – Each container can hold 1 kg of flour.

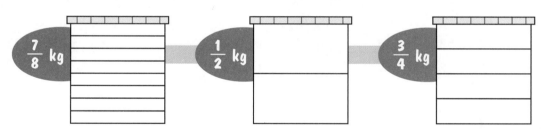

$\frac{7}{8}$ kg $\frac{1}{2}$ kg $\frac{3}{4}$ kg

Sugar – Each container can hold 1 kg of sugar.

$2\frac{4}{5}$ kg $2\frac{1}{3}$ kg $\frac{5}{2}$ kg

㉘ I want the container with the most flour and the group with the least sugar. Which container of flour and group of sugar should I take?

Decimals

I've coloured 0.995 of my cube.

- Write, compare, and order decimal numbers to thousandths.
- Understand the place value in decimal numbers.
- Round decimal numbers to the given places.

Write a decimal for each group of the diagrams to show how much is coloured. Then write the decimal in words.

①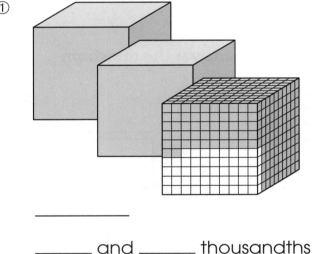

_____

_____ and _____ thousandths

②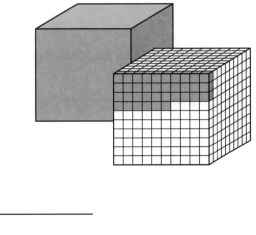

_____

_____ and _____ thousandths

Write the decimals in numerals or in words.

③ 4 and 62 thousandths _____

④ 6 and 5 thousandths _____

⑤ 3 and 123 thousandths _____

⑥ 10 and 4 thousandths _____

⑦ 5.273 _____

⑧ 3.018 _____

⑨ 8.176 _____

⑩ 7.009 _____

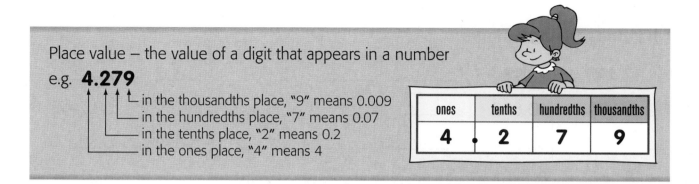

Place value – the value of a digit that appears in a number

e.g. **4.279**

— in the thousandths place, "9" means 0.009
— in the hundredths place, "7" means 0.07
— in the tenths place, "2" means 0.2
— in the ones place, "4" means 4

ones	tenths	hundredths	thousandths
4	2	7	9

Write the meaning of each digit in bold.

⑪ 3.**9**74 _____

⑫ 5.1**8**3 _____

⑬ 4.**2**71 _____

⑭ 8.16**8** _____

⑮ **7**.054 _____

⑯ 3.8**6**2 _____

⑰ 145.2**69** _____

⑱ 27.04**8** _____

⑲ 902.**5**43 _____

⑳ 163.5**74** _____

Write as decimals. Then draw lines to match the decimals that have the same value.

㉑

20 thousandths   2 tenths and 22 thousandths

222 thousandths   2 hundredths and 2 thousandths

22 thousandths   2 hundredths

202 thousandths   2 tenths and 2 hundredths

220 thousandths   2 tenths and 2 thousandths

Fill in the missing numbers.

㉒ 2.497   2.498   _____   _____   2.501   2.502   _____

㉓ 60.803   60.802   _____   _____   _____   60.798   60.797

㉔ 5.263   5.273   _____   _____   _____   5.313   5.323

㉕ 8.185   8.190   _____   _____   8.205   _____   8.215

㉖ 9.274   9.174   _____   _____   8.874   _____   8.674

Use arrows to mark the locations of the readings on the number lines. Then fill in the blanks to complete the sentences.

㉗

Ribbon	Length
A	3.974 m
B	3.978 m
C	3.986 m
D	3.98 m

3.974

3.97   3.98   3.99

_____ is the longest. It is _____ long.

㉘

Pot	Capacity
A	8.25 L
B	8.248 L
C	8.253 L
D	8.242 L

8.24   8.25   8.26

_____ has the greatest capacity. It can hold _____ of water.

㉙

Bag	Weight
A	5.224 kg
B	5.234 kg
C	5.228 kg
D	5.22 kg

5.22   5.23   5.24

_____ is the lightest. It weighs _____ .

Round the decimals.

Round the decimal to the nearest

	ones	tenths	hundredths
㉚ 6.274	_____	_____	_____
㉛ 10.168	_____	_____	_____
㉜ 7.593	_____	_____	_____
㉝ 6.412	_____	_____	_____
㉞ 8.996	_____	_____	_____
㉟ 12.954	_____	_____	_____

Look at the decimals given. Answer the questions.

6.761
6.734
3.284
5.598
7.006
7.258
6.886

㊱ Which decimals are smaller than 6.705?

_____

㊲ Which decimals have an "8" in their hundredths place?

_____

㊳

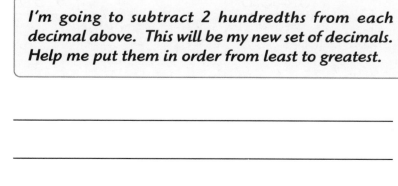

I'm going to subtract 2 hundredths from each decimal above. This will be my new set of decimals. Help me put them in order from least to greatest.

_____

_____

_____

Addition and Subtraction of Decimals

Score:
3.1 6 8
+ 5.2 7 3
———
8.4 4 1

- Add and subtract decimals to thousandths.
- Do estimates.
- Solve problems involving addition and subtraction of decimals.

If this ball lands in the centre, I'll have 8.441 points in all.

5.273
3.168
1.559

Put a decimal point in each answer to make the calculation true.

①
```
    4.5 7 4
+   2.6 5 3
————————
    7 2 2 7
```

②
```
    8.6 5 4
-   3.4 8
————————
    5 1 7 4
```

③
```
    2 9.6
-  1 2.8 6 4
————————
    1 6 7 3 6
```

④
```
    9.6 8
+   5.2 7 9
————————
   1 4 9 5 9
```

⑤
```
   1 0.0 0 4
-    7.3 7
————————
    2 6 3 4
```

⑥
```
    0.1 8 7
+   8.6 6
————————
    8 8 4 7
```

Find the answers.

⑦
```
    6.5 7 4
+   5.3 9 9
————————
```

⑧
```
    8.5 1 7
-   3.4 5 8
————————
```

⑨
```
    7.2 6
+   9.8 7 7
————————
```

⑩ 7.203 + 1.864 = _____

⑪ 5.392 + 12.569 = _____

⑫ 10.27 − 4.893 = _____

⑬ 8.106 − 2.97 = _____

⑭ 3.56 + 2.877 = _____

⑮ 0.184 + 1.83 = _____

⑯ 8.209 − 4.6 = _____

⑰ 5 − 2.731 = _____

Look at each group of items. Do the estimates and then find the exact answers.

⑱

Total Weight		Difference in Weight	
Estimate	Actual	Estimate	Actual

⑲

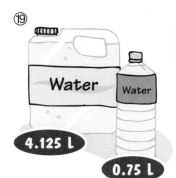

Total Capacity		Difference in Capacity	
Estimate	Actual	Estimate	Actual

⑳

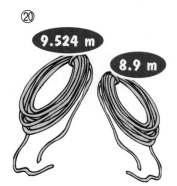

Total Length		Difference in Length	
Estimate	Actual	Estimate	Actual

Estimate and check the correct answers. Put a cross for the incorrect ones.

㉑ $15.273 + 8.169 =$ _234.42_ ◯

㉒ $527.684 - 188.5 =$ _339.184_ ◯

㉓ $10.31 - 5.649 =$ _0.466_ ◯

㉔ $63.57 + 396.251 =$ _459.821_ ◯

㉕ $7.594 + 8.86 =$ _16.454_ ◯

㉖ $200.143 + 45.987 =$ _246.13_ ◯

Fill in the missing numbers.

㉗
```
    5.■93
+  ■.5■8
───────────
  13.48■
```

㉘
```
    9.6■■
-  ■.■59
───────────
   5.474
```

㉙
```
   12.■0■
-  ■.1■7
───────────
   3.647
```

㉚
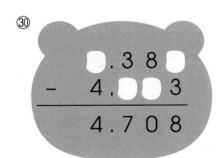
```
   ■.38■
-  4.■■3
───────────
   4.708
```

㉛
```
  ■.693
+ 6.2■7
───────────
 13.■5■
```

㉜
```
   2.■■3
+  ■.70■
───────────
  12.290
```

Look at the pictures. Complete the sentences.

㉝

46.253 kg

Sam

- Peter is 2.467 kg heavier than Sam.
- Bob is 1.635 kg lighter than Sam.

a. Peter weighs _____ and Bob weighs _____ .

b. Bob is lighter than Peter by _____ .

㉞

I am 1.165 m tall.

- Father Bear is 0.253 m taller than Mother Bear.
- Sister Bear is 0.68 m shorter than Father Bear.
- Mother Bear is 0.523 m taller than Brother Bear.

a. Father Bear is _____ tall.

b. Sister Bear is _____ tall.

c. Brother Bear is _____ tall.

Solve the problems.

㉟ Mrs. Green has bought 2 bags of treats weighing 3.593 kg and 4.082 kg. What is the total weight of the treats?

_____ = _____   _____

㊱ Mary walks 1.534 km in a given time. If Terry can walk 0.66 km farther than Mary, how far can Terry walk in the given time?

_____ = _____   _____

㊲ Aunt Sue cuts a 10-m-long ribbon into 2 pieces. If 1 piece of the ribbon is 4.186 m long, how long is the other piece?

_____ = _____   _____

㊳ The capacity of a jug is 2.64 L. If Mrs. Hall fills the jug with 1.374 L of orange juice, how much more juice can the jug hold?

_____ = _____   _____

The children are playing a game in which they each jump two times. Look at the record. Help the children complete the table and answer the question.

㊴

	John	Eva	Tina	Leo
1st jump (m)	1.008	0.962		0.982
2nd jump (m)		0.815	1.011	0.924
Total Distance (m)	2.31		2.08	

㊵

> *The one who jumps the farthest is the winner. Who is the winner?*

_____

Multiplication and Division of Decimals

Total weight:

$$\begin{array}{r} 1 \\ 1.6 \\ \times \quad 2 \\ \hline 3.2 \end{array}$$

I can move 3.2 kg of cheese cubes.

- Multiply and divide decimals to tenths by whole numbers.
- Multiply whole numbers by 0.1, 0.01, and 0.001 using mental strategies.
- Multiply and divide decimals by 10, 100, 1000, and 10 000 using mental strategies.

Write a decimal point in the correct place of each answer.

When a decimal to tenth is multiplied by a whole number, the answer should either be a decimal to tenth or a whole number.

$$\begin{array}{r} 5 \\ 2.8 \leftarrow \\ \times \quad 7 \quad \text{1 decimal place} \\ \hline 19.6 \leftarrow \\ \uparrow \\ \text{align} \end{array}$$

①
$$\begin{array}{r} 3.9 \\ \times \quad 4 \\ \hline 1\ 5\ 6 \end{array}$$

②
$$\begin{array}{r} 0.8 \\ \times \quad 3 \\ \hline 2\ 4 \end{array}$$

Do the multiplication.

③
$$\begin{array}{r} 2.9 \\ \times \quad 3 \\ \hline \end{array}$$

④
$$\begin{array}{r} 13.2 \\ \times \quad 6 \\ \hline \end{array}$$

⑤
$$\begin{array}{r} 5.4 \\ \times \quad 8 \\ \hline \end{array}$$

⑥ 9.7 x 5 = _____

⑦ 8.8 x 12 = _____

⑧ 5.3 x 24 = _____

⑨ 10.9 x 6 = _____

⑩ 8 aliens weigh _____ kg in all.

⑪ 15 aliens weigh _____ kg in all.

⑫ The height of a spaceship is 6 times the height of an alien. The spaceship is _____ m tall.

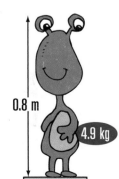

0.8 m

4.9 kg

Division of decimals:

1st Divide the same way as whole numbers.

2nd Put a decimal point in the quotient directly above the one in the dividend.

e.g. 41.6 ÷ 8 = _____

align

```
        5.2
    8 ) 4 1.6
        4 0
          1 6
          1 6
```

41.6 ÷ 8 = **5.2**

e.g. 30 ÷ 4 = _____

align

```
        7.5
    4 ) 3 0.0
        2 8
          2 0
          2 0
```

30 ÷ 4 = **7.5**

Do the division.

⑬

```
6 ) 9.6
```

⑭

```
7 ) 4 4.8
```

⑮

```
6 ) 7 5
```

⑯

```
1 8 ) 4 1.4
```

⑰

```
1 6 ) 1 7 4.4
```

⑱

```
2 8 ) 4 3 4
```

⑲   51.8 ÷ 7 = _____

⑳   156 ÷ 8   = _____

㉑   70.2 ÷ 9 = _____

㉒   127.6 ÷ 11 = _____

㉓

This cow produces 74.4 L of milk in 6 days.

How much milk does this cow produce daily?

_____ = _____   _____

Move the decimal point | e.g. Multiply 25 by 0.1, 0.01, or 0.001

a whole number
- x 0.1 ⟶ 1 place to the left
- x 0.01 ⟶ 2 places to the left
- x 0.001 ⟶ 3 places to the left

$25 \times 0.1 = $ **2.5** (2.5)

$25 \times 0.01 = $ **0.25** (0.25)

$25 \times 0.001 = $ **0.025** (0.025)

Check each answer. If the answer is correct, put a check mark in the circle; otherwise, put a cross and find the correct answer.

㉔ $94 \times 0.01 = $ _0.0094_ ⃝ _____

㉕ $56 \times 0.001 = $ _0.056_ ⃝ _____

㉖ $86 \times 0.1 = $ _0.86_ ⃝ _____

㉗ $90 \times 0.01 = $ _0.9_ ⃝ _____

㉘ $7 \times 0.1 = $ _0.7_ ⃝ _____

㉙ $43 \times 0.001 = $ _0.043_ ⃝ _____

㉚ $8 \times 0.01 = $ _0.08_ ⃝ _____

㉛ $50 \times 0.001 = $ _0.5_ ⃝ _____

Use a calculator to find the answers. Look for a pattern in each group of questions. Then do the coloured questions mentally.

㉜ $0.4 \times 10 = $ _____

$0.4 \times 100 = $ _____

$0.4 \times 1000 = $ _____

$0.4 \times 10\ 000 = $ _____

㉝ $8.5 \times 10 = $ _____

$8.5 \times 100 = $ _____

$8.5 \times 1000 = $ _____

$8.5 \times 10\ 000 = $ _____

㉞ $13.7 \times 10 = $ _____

$13.7 \times 100 = $ _____

$13.7 \times 1000 = $ _____

$13.7 \times 10\ 000 = $ _____

㉟ $200.6 \times 10 = $ _____

$200.6 \times 100 = $ _____

$200.6 \times 1000 = $ _____

$200.6 \times 10\ 000 = $ _____

Use a calculator to find the answers.   Look for a pattern in each group of questions. Then do the coloured questions mentally.

㊱ $3.6 \div 10$ = _____

$3.6 \div 100$ = _____

$3.6 \div 1000$ = _____

$3.6 \div 10\ 000$ = _____

㊲ $10.5 \div 10$ = _____

$10.5 \div 100$ = _____

$10.5 \div 1000$ = _____

$10.5 \div 10\ 000$ = _____

Solve the problems.

㊳

a. If it takes Susan 6 days to finish a box of cereal, how much cereal does Susan have every day on average?

_____ = _____   _____

b. How many kilograms do 9 boxes of cereal weigh?

_____ = _____   _____

㊴

18.7 cm

16 cm

a. What is the area of the rectangular sheet?

_____ = _____   _____

b. Jason is cutting the sheet into two pieces with the same size. What is the area of each piece?

_____ = _____   _____

㊵

The total weight of the pizzas is 1.8 kg. How heavy is each pizza?

_____ = _____

_____

Fractions, Decimals, and Percents

About 80% of the pop is still in the box.

- Understand the relationships among fractions, decimals, and percents.
- Solve simple problems related to percents.

Write the percent that represents the coloured part of each 100-square grid in two ways.

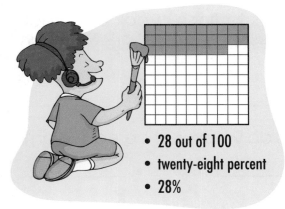

- 28 out of 100
- twenty-eight percent
- 28%

① **A** _____ ; _____

B _____ ; _____

C _____ ; _____

D _____ ; _____

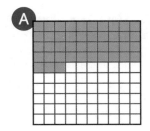

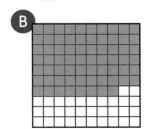

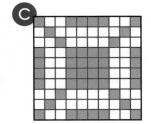

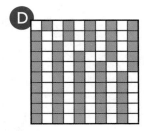

Colour the grid to match each given percent.

② **36%**
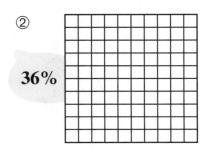

③ **72%**
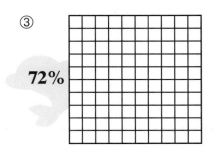

④ **15%**
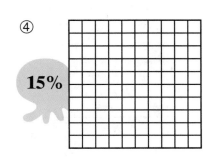

Estimate what percent of each circle is coloured.

⑤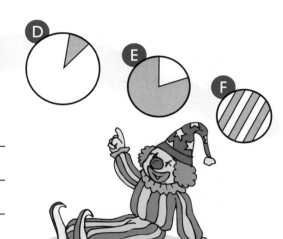

Ⓐ about _____   Ⓑ about _____

Ⓒ about _____   Ⓓ about _____

Ⓔ about _____   Ⓕ about _____

Look at the animals. Fill in the blanks with percents.

⑥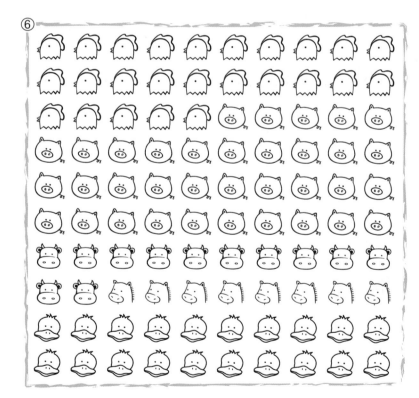

Animals on the Farm

- chickens: _____
- pigs: _____
- cows: _____
- horses: _____
- ducks: _____
- 4-legged animals: _____
- 2-legged animals: _____

⑦

Colour 20 of the animals above yellow and 37 of them green.

_____ of the animals are coloured.

 *A percent can also be expressed as a fraction or a decimal.*

e.g.

As a percent : 50%

As a fraction : $\frac{50}{100}$ or $\frac{1}{2}$

As a decimal : 0.5

Write each percent as a fraction with 100 in the denominator. Then write it in simplest form.

⑧ 40% = $\overline{100}$ = _____

⑨ 95% = _____ = _____

⑩ 54% = _____ = _____

⑪ 75% = _____ = _____

⑫ 66% = _____ = _____

⑬ 84% = _____ = _____

Write each percent as a fraction with 100 in the denominator. Then write it as a decimal.

⑭ 25% = $\overline{100}$

= _____

⑮ 96% = _____

= _____

⑯ 48% = _____

= _____

⑰ 65% = _____

= _____

⑱ 84% = _____

= _____

⑲ 70% = _____

= _____

Write each fraction or decimal as a percent.

⑳ $\frac{27}{100}$ = _____ %

㉑ $\frac{62}{100}$ = _____

㉒ $\frac{50}{100}$ = _____

㉓ 0.39 = _____ %

㉔ 0.91 = _____

㉕ 0.16 = _____

Check the correct descriptions of the use of percent in each situation.

㉖

Ⓐ A bonus bag holds as much as a regular bag plus 10 treats more.

Ⓑ A bonus bag holds 100 treats more than a regular bag.

Ⓒ A bonus bag holds as much as a regular bag plus $\frac{1}{10}$ more.

㉗

Ⓐ The cost of the dress is reduced by $2.

Ⓑ The dress costs $80 now.

Ⓒ The cost of the dress is reduced by $\frac{2}{10}$.

㉘

...90% chance of snow...

Ⓐ The chance of snowing is $\frac{9}{10}$.

Ⓑ It is probably going to snow.

Ⓒ It is probably not going to snow.

㉙

Ⓐ There are more big fish than small fish.

Ⓑ Half of the fish are big.

Ⓒ 0.5 of the fish are small.

50%: big fish
the rest: small fish

17

Unit Rates and Ratios

- Find the unit rate of 2 quantities with different units.
- Find the ratio of 2 quantities with the same unit.
- Solve problems involving unit rates and ratios.

Unit rate = $30 ÷ 15 bones
= $2/bone

15 bones for $30

Find the rates. Show your work.

①
Unit rate

= $ _____ ÷ _____ treats

= $ _____ /treat

② 750 mL
Unit rate

= _____

= _____

③ 882 g
Unit rate

= _____

= _____

④ 360 g 30
Unit rate

= _____

= _____

Find the rates.

⑤ Type 196 words in 2 minutes

_____ words/min

⑥ Sold 765 robots in 5 days

_____

⑦ Give 238 pencils to 17 children

_____

⑧ Put 758.4 kg of flour in 4 bags

_____

⑨
Put 250 light bulbs in 10 boxes.

_____

⑩ I run 44 km in 8 h.

_____

Find the unit price for each quantity. Then check the best buy.

⑪

(A) 5 cans for $4.10 = $ _____ /can

(B) 3 cans for $2.07 = _____

(C) 8 cans for $6.32 = _____

⑫

(A) 4 bottles for $10.60 = $ _____ /bottle

(B) 5 bottles for $13.90 = _____

(C) 2 bottles for $5.26 = _____

⑬

(A) 9 key chains for $42.93 = $ _____ /key chain

(B) 6 key chains for $30.72 = _____

(C) 8 key chains for $37.52 = _____

Read what the people say. Help them find their hourly rates and hours of work.

⑭ Hourly rate

a. Sam: $ _____ /h

b. Craig: $ _____ /h

⑮ Hours of work

a. Sam: _____ h/week

b. Craig: _____ h/week

I earn $540 in 40 hours and work 160 hours in 4 weeks.

I earn $307.20 in 24 hours and work 96 hours in 3 weeks.

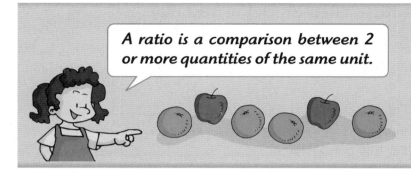

A ratio is a comparison between 2 or more quantities of the same unit.

Find the ratio of the number of apples to the number of oranges.

Apples : Oranges = 2:4

The ratio of the number of apples to the number of oranges is 2:4.

Look at the pictures. Write each ratio.

⑯

a. Pencils : Pens = _____

b. Crayons : Pencils = _____

c. Pens : All = _____

⑰

a. Animal stickers : Plant stickers = _____

b. Animal stickers : All = _____

c. Big stickers : Small stickers = _____

d. 3 stickers are yellow and the rest are red.

Yellow stickers : Red stickers = _____

⑱ a. Ted's acorns : Ray's acorns = _____

b. Ted's acorns : All = _____

c. If Ray gives 24 acorns to Ted, the ratio of Ted's acorns to Ray's acorns will be _____ .

I have 64 acorns.

I have 4 only.

A ratio can be written in different ways. e.g. 3 to 4, 3:4, or $\frac{3}{4}$

e.g.   No. of hearts : No. of squares
= 3:6
= 1:2 ← in simplest form

The ratio of the number of hearts to the number

of squares is 1 to 2 (1:2 or $\frac{1}{2}$).

To find equivalent ratios, multiply or divide each term by the same number other than 0.

e.g. $\frac{2}{7} = \frac{2 \times 2}{7 \times 2} = \frac{4}{14}$

$\frac{2}{7}$ and $\frac{4}{14}$ are equivalent ratios.

Circle the equivalent ratios in each group.

⑲
2:3
3:5   8:12

⑳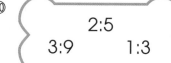
2:5
3:9   1:3

㉑
3:4
4:5   8:10

Write each ratio in simplest form.

㉒ 20:80 _____ ㉓ 6:9 _____ ㉔ 5:10 _____

㉕ 12:24 _____ ㉖ 12:20 _____ ㉗ 4:26 _____

Solve the problems. Write the answers in simplest form.

㉘ Colour 4 bones green, 6 bones yellow, and the rest red. Then find the ratios.

a. Yellow bones : All = _____

b. Red bones   : All = _____

㉙
If I have two more big bones, what will be the ratio of the number of big bones to the number of small bones?

_____

18

1.26 m = 1.26 x 100 cm
= 126 cm

Wow! You're 126 cm long!

1.26 m

Unit Conversions

- Do unit conversions.
- Solve problems requiring conversion from larger to smaller metric units.

Write the measurements in decimals with the help of the charts.

 **Weight**

① 3 kg 16 g

= _____ g

kg	g		

② 4 g 300 mg

= _____ mg

g	mg		

③ 5 kg 620 g

= _____ g

kg	g		

④ 8 g 25 mg

= _____ mg

g	mg		

Length or distance

⑤ 2 km 16 m

= _____ m

km	m		

⑥ 3 m 16 cm

= _____ cm

m	cm	

⑦ 7 cm 5 mm

= _____ mm

cm	mm

⑧ 5 km 9 m

= _____ m

km	m		

Capacity

⑨

1 L 25 mL

L	mL		

_____ mL

⑩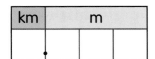

Spring Water
3 L 600 mL

L	mL		

_____ mL

Changing to a smaller unit: use "**x**"

4.52 kg

= 4.52 x 1000 g

= **4520 g**

Changing to a larger unit: use "**÷**"

255 mL

= 255 ÷ 1000 L

= **0.255 L**

Do the unit conversions by changing the large units to small units. Show your work.

⑪ 1.06 kg

= _____ x 1000 g

= _____

⑫  2.39 m

= _____ x 100 cm

= _____

⑬ 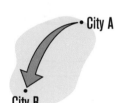 2.75 L

= _____ x 1000 mL

= _____

⑭ •City A 3.28 km

= _____ x 1000 m

•City B = _____

⑮ 4.9 cm

= _____ x 10 mm

= _____

⑯ 0.3 L

= _____ x 1000 mL

= _____

Do the unit conversions by changing the small units to large units. Show your work.

⑰ 5065 g

= _____ ÷ 1000 kg

= _____

⑱ 3925 mL

= _____ ÷ 1000 L

= _____

⑲ 866 m

= _____ ÷ 1000 km

= _____

⑳ 72 cm

= _____ ÷ 100 m

= _____

㉑ 480 g

= _____ ÷ 1000 kg

= _____

㉒ 67 mm

= _____ ÷ 10 cm

= _____

Write each measurement with the given unit. Then put the things in order.

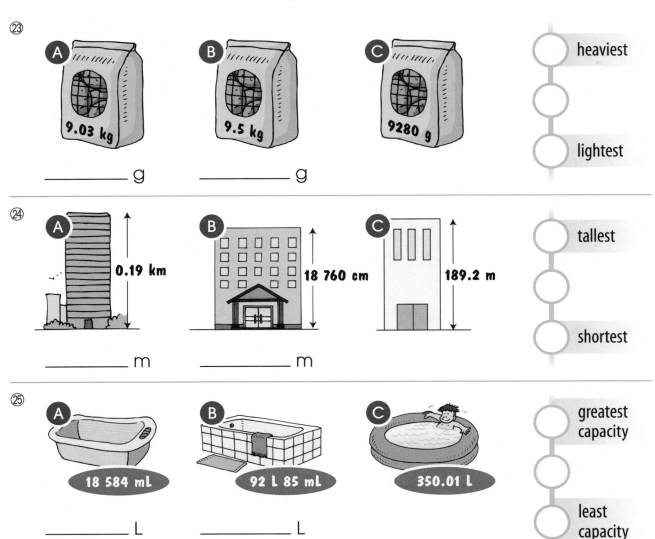

23 A 9.03 kg   B 9.5 kg   C 9280 g

_____ g   _____ g

heaviest

lightest

24 A 0.19 km   B 18 760 cm   C 189.2 m

_____ m   _____ m

tallest

shortest

25 A 18 584 mL   B 92 L 85 mL   C 350.01 L

_____ L   _____ L

greatest capacity

least capacity

Circle the greater one in each group.

26 8 L 25 mL
    8039 mL

27 7 km 16 m
    70 086 m

28 6 cm 9 mm
    82 mm

29 40 m 19 cm
    409 cm

30 1763 m
    1.695 km

31 89.5 kg
    90 024 g

Solve the problems with the help of the clues. Show your work.

③②

How many grams are there in one serving if 1.5 kg of ham serves six people?

• Write the amount in grams.
• Use division.

There are _____ g in one serving.

③③

How many millilitres do I need to paint 5 doors if I use 0.57 L of paint for one door?

• Write the amount in millilitres.
• Use multiplication.

_____

③④
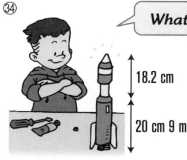

What is the height of my rocket in centimetres?

18.2 cm

20 cm 9 mm

• Write the height in decimals.
• Use addition.

_____

③⑤

Ivan's brother is 126 cm long. How long is Ivan in centimetres?

• Write the length in centimetres.
• Use subtraction.

Ivan

I'm 0.19 m shorter than my brother.

_____

2-D Shapes (1)

Turn clockwise:

The order of rotational symmetry of this bone is 2.

- Sort and classify quadrilaterals by geometric properties related to symmetry, angles, and sides.
- Sort polygons according to the number of lines of symmetry and the orders of rotational symmetry.

Draw any two quadrilaterals with the given number of lines of symmetry.

① with 1 line of symmetry

② with 2 lines of symmetry

Draw any two quadrilaterals with the given number of right angles.

③ with 1 right angle

④ with 4 right angles

Colour the quadrilaterals with two pairs of parallel sides.

⑤

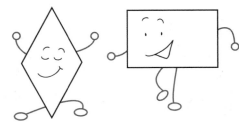

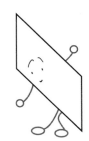

Draw the missing side of each quadrilateral. Measure and label the sides and angles. Name it. Then answer the questions.

⑥

I am a _____ .

I am a _____ .

I am a _____ .

I am a _____ .

I am a _____ .

⑦ Which quadrilateral(s) has / have

a. four right angles? _____

b. opposite sides parallel? _____

c. opposite angles equal? _____

d. one pair of parallel sides? _____

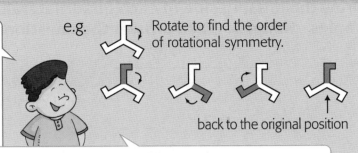

A figure has rotational symmetry if it fits on itself within a complete rotation. The order of rotational symmetry is the number of times the figure fits on itself in one complete rotation.

Rotate to find the order of rotational symmetry.

back to the original position

This shape fits on itself 3 times in one rotation; it has rotational symmetry of order of 3.

Draw the lines of symmetry.

⑧ 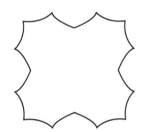   ⑨ 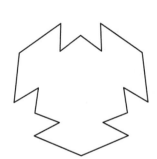   ⑩

Check the polygons that have rotational symmetry.

⑪

Ⓐ   Ⓑ   Ⓒ

Ⓓ   Ⓔ   Ⓕ

Write the order of rotational symmetry for each polygon.

⑫ 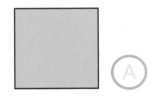   ⑬ 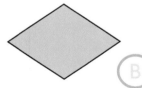   ⑭    ⑮

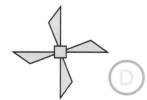

Look at the polygons. Complete the table.

⑯

	A	B	C	D	E
Has line(s) of symmetry (✔/✘) If so, how many?					
Has rotational symmetry (✔/✘) If so, what order?					

Draw a polygon to match each description. Label it with the given letter. Then answer the question.

⑰

A a polygon that has 4 lines of symmetry and has rotational symmetry of order of 4

B a polygon that has 1 line of symmetry, but has no rotational symmetry

⑱

If a shape has rotational symmetry, it also has lines of symmetry. Am I correct?

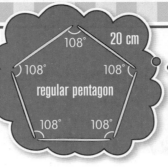

2-D Shapes (2)

- Measure, construct, and classify angles up to 180° using a protractor.
- Construct polygons with the given angle and side measurements.

108°   20 cm

108°   108°

regular pentagon

108°   108°

I'm making a regular pentagonal frame. Each side is 20 cm long and each angle is 108˚.

Name, measure, and record the angles of each polygon. Then classify each angle as acute, right, or obtuse.

①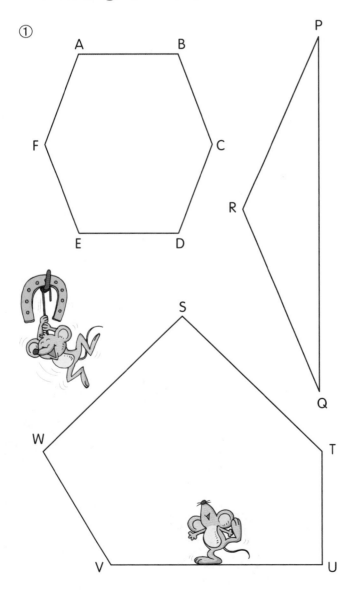

The hexagon:

∠A = _____ ; _____ angle

∠B = _____ ; _____

∠C = _____ ; _____

∠D = _____ ; _____

∠E = _____ ; _____

∠F = _____ ; _____

The triangle:

∠P = _____ ; _____ angle

∠Q = _____ ; _____

∠R = _____ ; _____

The pentagon:

∠S = _____ ; _____ angle

∠T = _____ ; _____

∠U = _____ ; _____

∠V = _____ ; _____

∠W = _____ ; _____

Measure and record each angle. Classify the angle as acute, right, obtuse, or straight. Then construct an angle to match the description.

② an angle that has the same size

③ an angle that is 10° greater

④ an angle that is 15° smaller

⑤ an angle that is one half of this one and one angle that is one third

Read what the children say. Draw the regular polygons.

⑥
Each of the angles in an equilateral triangle is 60°. Draw an equilateral triangle with a side length of 4 cm.

⑦
Each of the angles in a square is a right angle. Draw a square with a side length of 3.8 cm.

⑧
The angles of a regular pentagon are all 108°. Draw a regular pentagon with a side length of 2.6 cm.

⑨
The angles of a regular hexagon are all 120°. Draw a regular hexagon with a side length of 2.2 cm.

⑩
The measure of each angle of a regular octagon is 135°. Draw two regular octagons with a side length of 2 cm and 1.8 cm respectively.

Construct the triangles with the given angles and sides. Then find the other two angles and the sum of the angles in each triangle.

⑪

A

∠ABC = 50°	BC = 5 cm
∠A =	∠C =
Sum of all ∠ =	

A

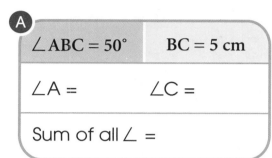

B

∠LMN = 74°	MN = 6.5 cm
∠L =	∠N =
Sum of all ∠ =	

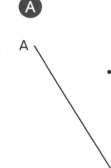

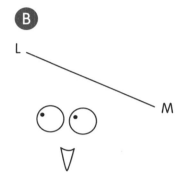

C

∠STU = 116°	TU = 6.6 cm
∠S =	∠U =
Sum of all ∠ =	

C

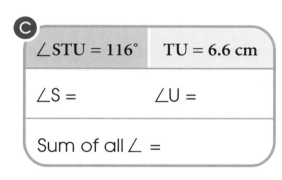

⑫

Do you think that the sum of the angles in a triangle must be equal to 180°?

3-D Figures

- Draw different views of a structure built by interlocking cubes.
- Draw 3-D figures built with interlocking cubes from the given top, side, and front views.

Draw the missing cubes to complete the views of the structures.

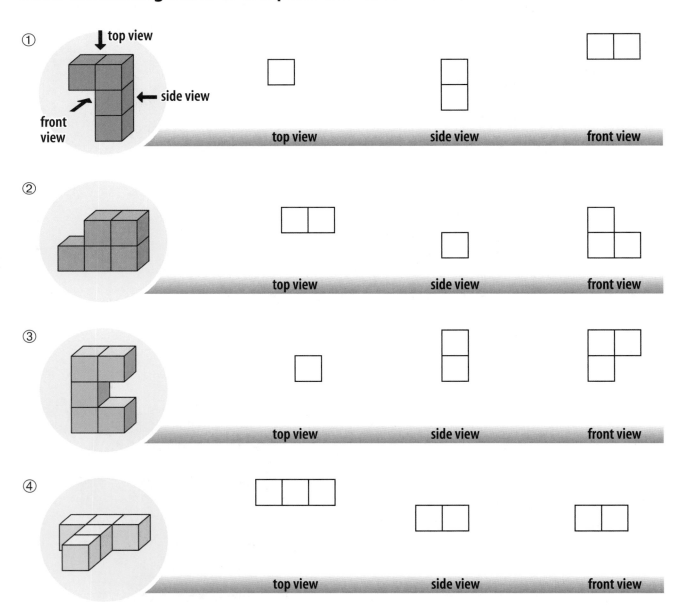

Draw the top, side, and front views of the structures made up of 6 interlocking cubes. Then label the views.

⑤ a.

_____

b.

_____

c.

_____

d.

Find the structures that have the given views. Write the letters.

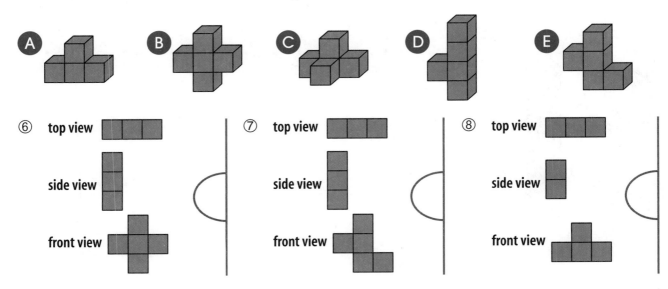

Ⓐ   Ⓑ   Ⓒ   Ⓓ   Ⓔ

⑥ top view   ⑦ top view   ⑧ top view

side view   side view   side view

front view   front view   front view

Draw the missing cubes to complete the drawings of the models made up of 7 interlocking cubes.

⑨

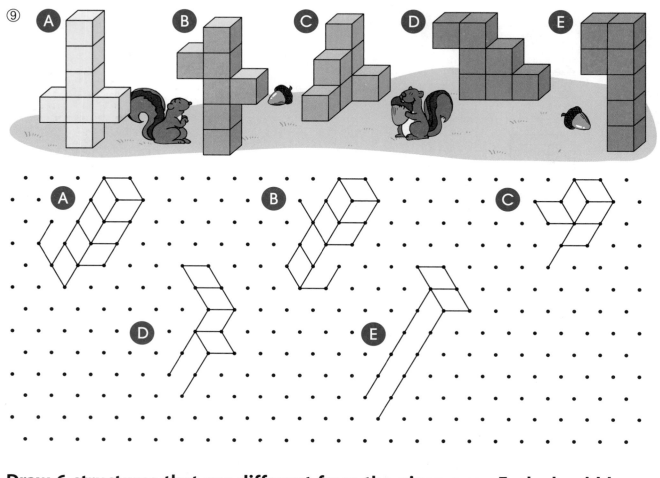

Draw 6 structures that are different from the given one. Each should have 6 interlocking cubes.

⑩

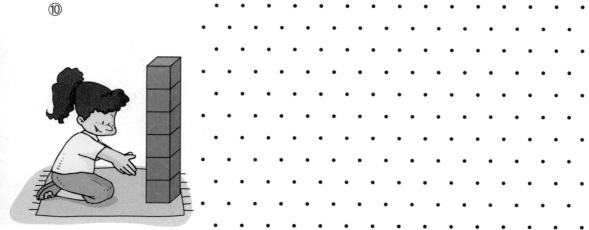

MATHEMATICS

Draw lines to match the views with the structures. Then draw the missing views.

⑪

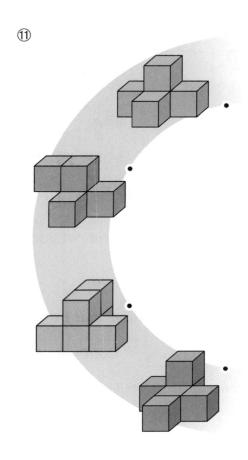

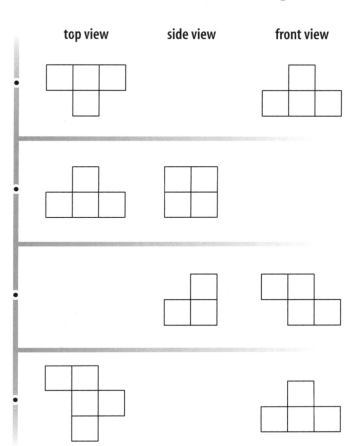

top view   side view   front view

Look at the top, side, and front views of each model. Then draw the model.

⑫

top view	side view	front view

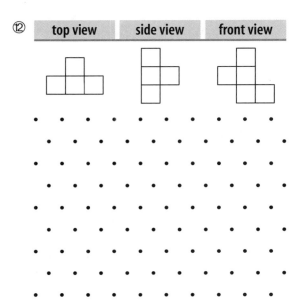

⑬

top view   side view   front view

Complete Canadian Curriculum • Grade 6   **89**

Transformations

- Identify and draw the missing parts of a rotation image.
- Describe different kinds of rotation with the centre of rotation inside or outside a shape.
- Complete and analyze designs made by reflecting, translating, or rotating shapes.

Hey! That's rotation.

Circle the correct words to complete what David says. Then check the rotation images of the pictures on the left.

①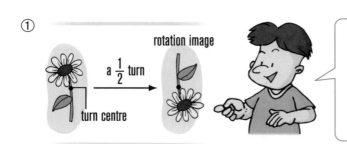

A rotation is a transformation that turns a shape about a **moving / fixed** point to form a **congruent / similar** shape.

②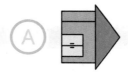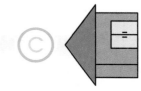

③

④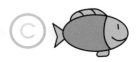

Each pair of pictures shows a rotation. Describe the rotations with the help of the given words.

clockwise rotation of 90° ↰   rotation of 180° ↻   counterclockwise rotation of 90° ↲

⑤    rotation image

_____

⑥   rotation image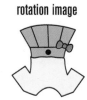

_____

⑦   rotation image

_____

⑧   rotation image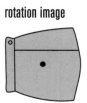

_____

Draw the missing parts of the rotation images. Then describe the rotations.

⑨

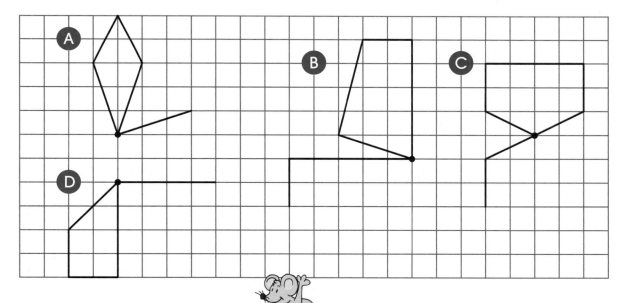

Description

 _____   _____

 _____   _____

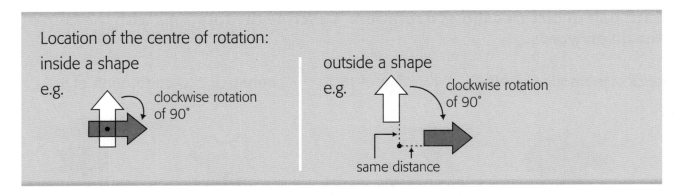

Location of the centre of rotation:

inside a shape

e.g.   clockwise rotation of 90°

outside a shape

e.g.   clockwise rotation of 90°

same distance

Draw the rotation images of each pair of shapes.

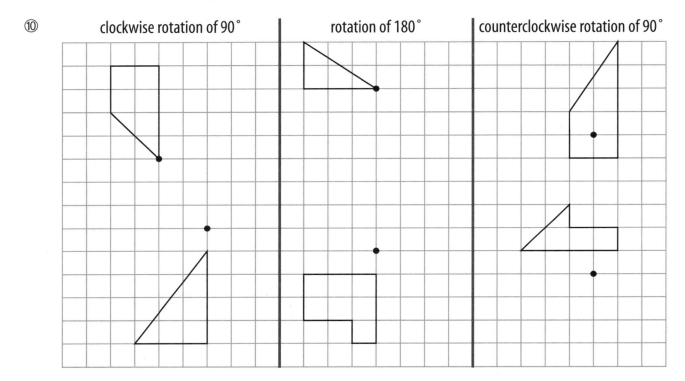

⑩   clockwise rotation of 90°   rotation of 180°   counterclockwise rotation of 90°

Use a red coloured pencil to mark the centre of rotation of each pair of shapes.

⑪

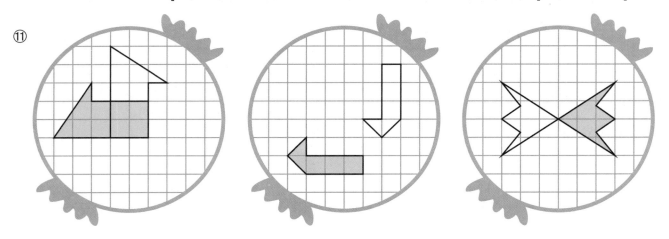

See how John designed different patterns with a single tile pattern. Complete his designs. Then tell what transformations are used in each case.

⑫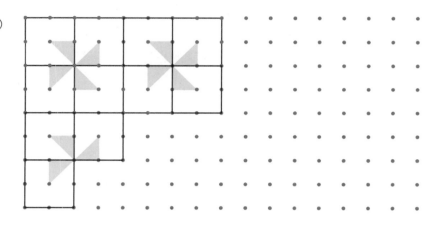

By _____

⑬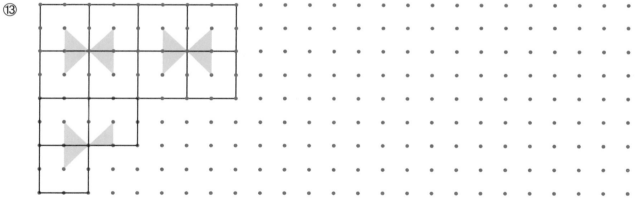

By _____

⑭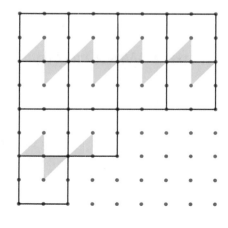

By _____

_____

Coordinate System

- Write the location of an object in a coordinate system.
- Locate an object in a coordinate system.
- Solve problems related to coordinate systems.

Beaver, can you see that the church is at (2,1)?

Read what the bird says. Help her find the coordinates of the animals. Then answer the questions.

To locate a point in a coordinate system, the first coordinate is the horizontal position and the second coordinate is the vertical position. The worm is at (1,2).

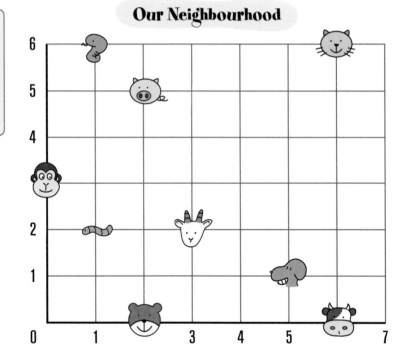

Our Neighbourhood

① **Positions of the Animals**

a. the cat (_____ ,6)

b. the dog (5, _____)

c. the snake (1, _____)

d. the monkey (_____ ,3)

e. the bear (_____ ,0)

f. the cow (6, _____)

g. the goat (3, _____)

h. the pig (_____ ,5)

② How many animals are there on the horizontal axis? What are they?

_____ ; _____

③ How many animals are there on the vertical axis? What are they?

_____ ; _____

Find the coordinates of the fish. Then answer the questions.

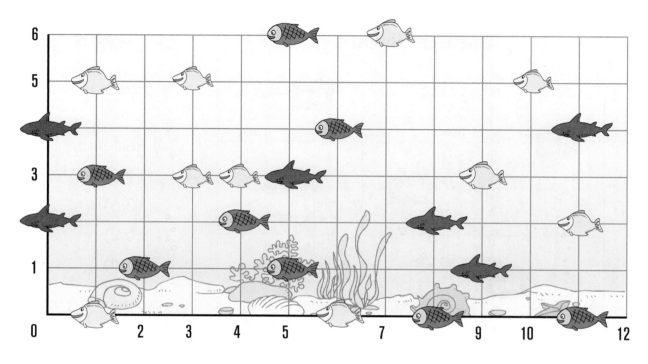

④

_____   _____   _____

_____   _____   _____

_____   _____   _____

_____   _____   _____

⑤   Which fish is closest to the shark at (11,4)?   _____

⑥   Which fish is closest to the fish at (1,0)?   _____

⑦   Which shark is closest to the shark at (8,2)?   _____

⑧   If the sharks can only swim forward, which shark will eat the most fish? How many fish will it get?

_____

Draw pictures to plot the things on the grid. Then answer the questions.

⑨

Spencers Town

Legend

- • Bus stop

🍴 Restaurant

(1,0)

(3,6)

(6,2)

(8,4)

🍎 Grocery store

(3,3)

(5,0)

(8,5)

⑩ What are the coordinates of the bus stops?

_____

_____

⑪ Each child wants to go to the closest bus stop. Which stop should each child go to?

Sue: the one at _____   **Sam**: _____

Gary: _____   **Jane**: _____

⑫

I go to the mall by bus. At which bus stop should I get off? Then which way should I go to get to the mall?

_____

Plot each group of points on the grid. Join the points to plot the shape of each stage. Name and find the area.

Stage 1
A(4,1)
B(10,1)   C(10,4)

Stage 2
P(5,9)   Q(5,5)
R(10,5)   S(10,9)

Stage 3
E(1,5)   F(0,0)
G(3,0)   H(4,5)

⑬

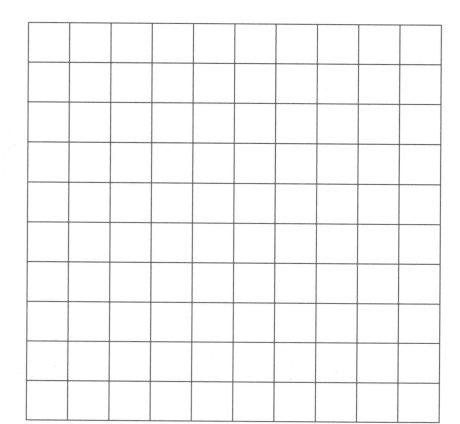

⑭

	Stage 1	Stage 2	Stage 3
Shape			
Area (square units)			

⑮

We'll have a show on the stage with the greatest area. If we need to skate 30 times around it, how far do we go?

_____

Patterning

- Identify geometric patterns and represent them numerically.
- Make tables of values for the number patterns described, in words, and then list the ordered pairs and plot the points on a graph.
- Describe pattern rules in words and find a term number or a term by extending patterns.
- Solve problems using patterning.

Term number	Term
1	2
2	4
3	6
4	8
5	10
6	12
7	14

Start with 2 beads and add 2 to each string to get the next string.

Follow the pattern to draw the next group. Then represent the pattern numerically.

①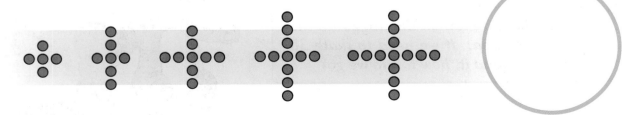

Number pattern: _____

②

Number pattern: _____

③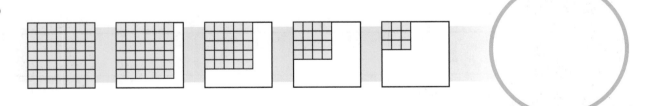

Number pattern: _____

Write the pattern rule in words and find the 15th term.
5000, 4750, 4500, 4250, 4000, 3750,...

5000 4750 4500...
−250   −250   −250

Pattern rule:
Start with 5000 and subtract 250 each time to get the next term.

The 15th term: 5000 − 250 x (15 − 1) ← There are 14 differences in all.
        = 1500

Find and write the pattern rules in words. Then answer the questions.

④   1, 3, 5, 7, 9, 11, 13,...

   a. Pattern rule: _____

   b. What is the 16th term?   _____

   c. What is the term number when the term is 39?   _____

⑤   120, 116, 112, 108, 104, 100, 96,...

   a. Pattern rule: _____

   b. What is the 12th term?   _____

   c. What is the term number when the term is 40?   _____

⑥   2, 4, 8, 16, 32, 64, 128,...

   a. Pattern rule: _____

   b. What is the 10th term?   _____

   c. What is the term number when the term is 16 384?   _____

⑦   24 576, 12 288, 6144, 3072, 1536, 768, 384,...

   a. Pattern rule: _____

   b. What is the 10th term?   _____

   c. What is the term number when the term is 12?   _____

Read what the animals say. Make a table of values for each number pattern.
Plot the points on the graph and draw a line to join the points. Then use the
graphs to answer the questions.

⑧ Start with 5 and add 3 to each term to get the next term.

Term number	Term	Ordered pairs
1	5	(1,5)
2	8	(2,8)
3	11	
4		
5		

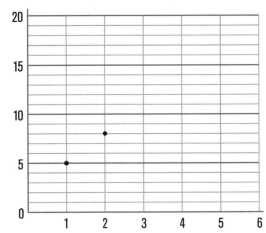

 If the term number is 6, what is the term? _____

⑨ Start with 50 and subtract 5 from each term to get the next term.

Term number	Term	Ordered pairs
1		
2		
3		
4		
5		
6		

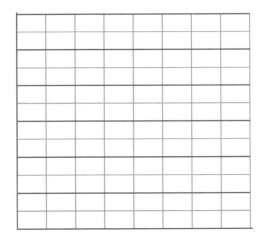

 If the term is 15, what is the term number? _____

Read what the children say. Help them complete the tables of values and graphs. Then answer the questions.

⑩

> I have 5 marbles in the 1st week. Each week after that I will buy 3 more marbles than the week before. How many marbles will I buy in the 9th week?

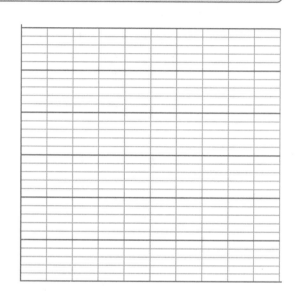

Term number	Term	Ordered pairs

He will buy _____ marbles in the 9th week.

⑪

> I have 260 beads. If I use 20 beads to make one necklace, how many beads will I have left after making 7 necklaces?

Term number	Term	Ordered pairs
1	240	(1,240)

She will have _____ beads left.

Simple Equations

- Identify variables and constants in equations.
- Solve problems that use two or three symbols or letters as variables to represent different unknown quantities.
- Solve simple equations with one variable.

Look at the formulas. Circle the variables and underline the constants. Then find the values of the unknowns.

① $A = (b \times h) \div 2$

A: Area of a triangle
b: base,   *h*: height

a. When $b = 10$, $h = 8$

$A = (\underline{\hspace{0.5cm}} \times \underline{\hspace{0.5cm}}) \div 2$

$= \underline{\hspace{1cm}}$

b. When $b = 12$, $h = 20$

$A = (\underline{\hspace{0.5cm}} \times \underline{\hspace{0.5cm}}) \div 2$

$= \underline{\hspace{1cm}}$

② $C = \$100 - \$9 \times y$

C: Change
y: no. of boxes of cookies

a. When $y = 8$

$C = \$100 - \$9 \times \underline{\hspace{0.5cm}}$

b. When $y = 11$

$C =$

③ $N = 20 \times m + 8 \times n$

N: Total no. of bones
m: no. of big bags,   *n*: no. of small bags

a. When $m = 3$, $n = 1$

$N =$

b. When $m = 2$, $n = 6$

$N =$

Big Bag : 20
Small Bag : 8

Solving problems using substitution:

e.g.

If n + 1 = 15 and n + 1 + s = 19, what value does s represent?

We know that $n + 1 = 15$.

$n + 1 + s = 19$ ← Think what number plus 15 is 19.

$15 + s = 19$

$s = 4$

Find the value of x in each equation.

④
$y - 5 = 11$

$y - 5 + x = 20$

_____ + x = _____

x = _____

⑤
$m \times 6 = 70$

$m \times 6 \div x = 10$

⑥ $12 + k = 40$

$12 + k - x = 35$

⑦ $b \div 8 = 24$

$x \times (b \div 8) = 48$

⑧ $14 - u = 9$

$x + (14 - u) = 25$

Rearrange or group the terms. Then find the value of y in each equation.

⑨ $3 + y + k = 9$

$k + 3 = 9$

⑩ $y + u - 2 - 4 = 16$

$u - 6 = 10$

⑪ $b \times (2 \times 3) - y = 4$

$b \times 6 = 12$

⑫ $y \div (m \div 5) = 4 + 5$

$m \div 5 = 3$

Solve the equations.

⑬ $9 + k = 50$

k = _____

⑭ $16 - y = 9$

y = _____

⑮ $m \div 3 = 24$

m = _____

⑯ $b \times 6 = 30$

b = _____

⑰ $c - 7 = 25$

c = _____

⑱ $x + 7 = 21$

x = _____

⑲ $16 = 27 - n$

n = _____

⑳ $42 = p \times 3$

p = _____

㉑ $30 = 60 \div u$

u = _____

Read what the children say.   Use equations to solve the problems.

㉒ a.

I have 20 party hats. If I use n party hats, how many party hats will be left?

No. of party hats left =

b.

If there are 4 party hats left, how many party hats have been used?

㉓ a.

Jenny gives each of her guests 6 candies. If she invites y friends to her party, how many candies in all will she give to her friends?

Total no. of candies =

b.

If she gives out 96 candies in all, how many guests are there?

Solve equations using guess-and-test method.

e.g. $2 \times n + 3 = 11$

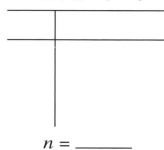

n is 4.

n	$2 \times n + 3$
1	$2 \times 1 + 3 = 5$ ✗ (not 11)
2	$2 \times 2 + 3 = 7$ ✗ (not 11)
3	$2 \times 3 + 3 = 9$ ✗ (not 11)
4	$2 \times 4 + 3 = 11$ ✔

Solve the equations.

㉔ $3 \times y - 1 = 17$

y	$3 \times y - 1$

$y = $ _____

㉕ $m \div 6 + 4 = 64$

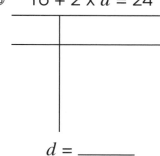

$m = $ _____

㉖ $42 \div n - 3 = 3$

$n = $ _____

㉗ $18 + a \div 3 = 28$

$a = $ _____

㉘ $16 + 2 \times d = 24$

$d = $ _____

㉙ $e \times 4 - 6 = 26$

$e = $ _____

Read what the boy says. Use an equation to solve the problem.

㉚

I pay 50 coins for 1 cow and 4 chickens. A cow costs 26 coins. How much does a chicken cost?

A chicken costs _____ coins.

Graphs (1)

Run faster, Sam! Don't you remember that you can go 100 m in 19 s?

- Read, describe, and interpret data presented in charts and graphs, including continuous line graphs.

The bar graph shows the effect of fertilizers on the growth of a vine over four weeks. Look at the graph and answer the questions.

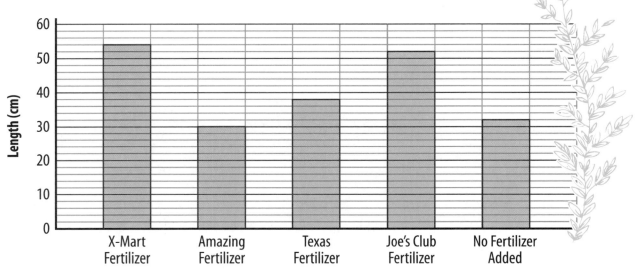

The Effect of Different Fertilizers on Vine Growth

① Which brand of fertilizer is the best? _____

② How much did the vine grow with no fertilizer added? _____

③ How much did the vine grow with Texas Fertilizer added? _____

④ Which brand of fertilizer should not be recommended? Explain.

_____

_____

⑤ On average, how much did the vine grow weekly

    a. with Joe's Club Fertilizer? _____

    b. with no fertilizer added? _____

⑥ On average, how much did the vine grow daily

    a. with X-Mart Fertilizer?

        Ⓐ about 2 cm   Ⓑ about 1 cm   Ⓒ 1 cm

    b. with Amazing Fertilizer?

        Ⓐ about 2 cm   Ⓑ about 1 cm   Ⓒ 3 cm

    c. with no fertilizer added?

        Ⓐ about 1 mm   Ⓑ about 11 mm   Ⓒ about 0.5 m

Look at the picture below and the bar graph on the previous page again. Complete the chart and answer Uncle Roy's question.

⑦ *I need to buy fertilizers for my landscaping company. Which brand of fertilizer should I buy? Explain.*

$19 Joe's Club Fertilizer

10 kg

X-Mart Fertilizer

Texas Fertilizer

$25 10 kg

$9 5 kg

a.

	Unit Price	Vine Growth Over 4 Weeks
X-Mart Fertilizer	$ /kg	cm
Texas Fertilizer	$ /kg	cm
Joe's Club Fertilizer	$ /kg	cm

b. _____

_____

_____

Kevin recorded yesterday's temperatures from 6:00 a.m. to 6:00 p.m on a line graph. Use his graph to answer the questions.

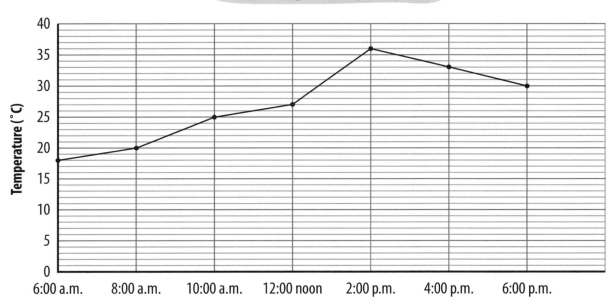

Yesterday's Temperatures

⑧   What time was the temperature highest?

_____

⑨   What was the temperature at 12:00 noon?

_____

⑩   What was the temperature at 3:00 p.m.?

_____

⑪   Describe the temperature change from 6:00 a.m. to 2:00 p.m.

_____

⑫   Describe the temperature change from 2:00 p.m. to 6:00 p.m.

_____

⑬   What was the difference in temperature at 6 o'clock in the morning and 6 o'clock in the evening?   _____

Jackson used a graph to show the number of apple pies made and sold on his farm in the past ten weeks. Read the graph. Then answer the questions.

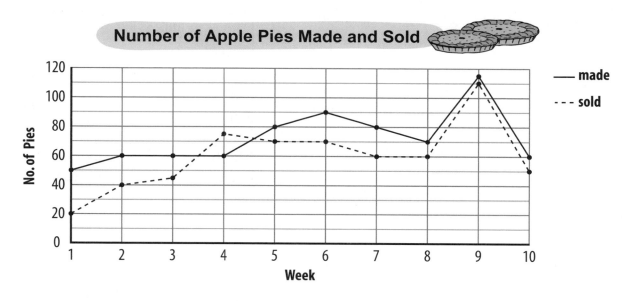

⑭ Jackson has mixed up his data for one of the weeks. Which week is it? What should the data be?

_____

⑮

Week	No. of Apple Pies Left
1	
2	
3	
4	
5	
6	
7	
8	
9	
10	

⑯ In which week do you see the smallest difference between the number of apple pies made and the number of apple pies sold?

_____

⑰ *The number of apple pies made and sold was exceptionally high in week 9. Can you tell me why?*

Jackson's Farm

_____

_____

_____

Graphs (2)

- Choose an appropriate type of graph to present a set of data.
- Make graphs to show data.
- Draw conclusions or describe the shape of a set of data presented in any graph.

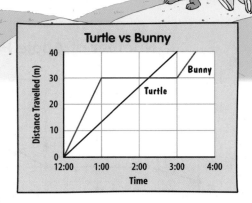

I'm 30 minutes faster.

Choose a graph that best presents each set of data below.

pictograph   stem-and-leaf plot   double bar graph

bar graph   broken-line graph   continuous line graph

① Comparison of the heights of five children _____

② Temperatures in Toronto yesterday _____

③ Number of boxes of cookies sold each month last year _____

④ Scores of Grade 6 students in a Math quiz _____

⑤ Comparison of the sales figures of two types of chips each day last week _____

⑥ Favourite snacks of the junior kindergarten children in Mrs. Green's class _____

⑦ *Changes in my dog's weight during the first year* _____

⑧ *Number of treats my dog ate each day last month* _____

Look at Judy's scores in different subjects. Help her complete the bar graphs to show her scores. Then answer the questions.

Language	Math	French	Science	Drama
84	96	63	72	80

⑨

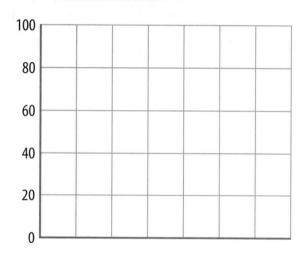

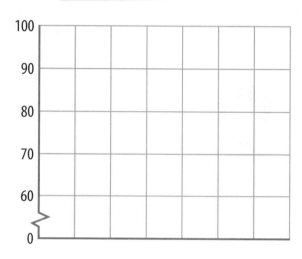

⑩ What is Judy's average score? _____

⑪ In which subject does Judy have the highest score? _____

⑫ Describe the scale of the graphs.

Ⓐ _____ Ⓑ _____

⑬ If Judy wants to show her parents that she did especially well in Math this semester, which graph should she use? Why?

_____

⑭ If Judy wants to show her friends that she is an all-round student, which graph should she use? Why?

_____

Ray and Tina did a survey to find out how much time the children spent on the Internet last week. Help them complete the stem-and-leaf plots. Then complete the chart and answer the questions.

> You can use a calculator to help you find the answer.

⑮

Ray's Record (in hours)

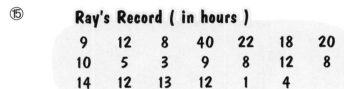

9	12	8	40	22	18	20
10	5	3	9	8	12	8
14	12	13	12	1	4	

Time Spent (h) on the Internet Last Week

Stem	Leaves
0	
1	
2	
4	

⑯

Tina's Record (in hours)

21	20	18	12	17	18	12	16	30	14	13	7	9
12	26	28	20	19	8	6	4	16	24	32	18	25
29	8	10	20	24	13	29	21	32	16	30	32	13
29	14	6	8	21	16	28	34	30	9	33		

Time Spent (h) on the Internet Last Week

Stem	Leaves
0	
1	
2	
3	

⑰ Complete the stem-and-leaf plot to show all the data collected by Ray and Tina.

Time Spent (h) on the Internet Last Week

Stem	Leaves
0	
1	
2	
3	
4	

⑱

	Mean	Median	Mode	Range
Ray's data				
Tina's data				
Ray & Tina's data				

⑲ What conclusion can you draw from the plots above?

_____

_____

_____

_____

_____

⑳

> *What conclusion can you draw from Ray and Tina's stem-and-leaf plot?*

_____

_____

Probability

The probability of getting a  star is $\frac{1}{40}$. I'm so lucky!

- Express theoretical probability as a ratio of the number of favourable outcomes to the total number of possible outcomes.
- Write the probability of an outcome using a value from the range of 0 to 1.
- Predict the frequency of an outcome in a simple probability experiment.

Congratulations! You can have a prize.

List all the possible outcomes for each probability experiment. Then write a fraction to describe the probability of each outcome.

①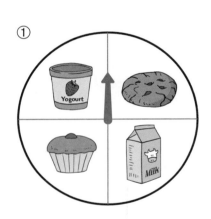

Spin the spinner once.

Possible outcomes: _____

What is the probability of landing on

a. "yogourt"? _____

b. "cookie"? _____

c. a dairy product? _____

②

Roll a dice.

Possible outcomes: _____

What is the probability of landing on

a. 3? _____

b. 1 or 2? _____

c. an odd number? _____

d. a number greater than 3? _____

e. a number greater than 6? _____

Read what the people say. Help them circle the best answer to describe the probability of each event.

③

> *There are 3 different colours of gumballs. Most of the gumballs are green and some are blue. But there is only one red gumball.*

The probability of getting

a. a green gumball $\frac{1}{3}$ $\frac{4}{5}$ $\frac{1}{2}$

b. a yellow gumball 0 $\frac{2}{3}$ 1

c. a red gumball $\frac{3}{4}$ $\frac{1}{5}$ $\frac{1}{50}$

④

> *We have four different combos to serve our customers. From our records, most customers like combo 1. About the same number of customers like either combo 2 or combo 4. Combo 3 is the least popular.*

The probability of the first customer choosing

a. combo 2 $\frac{4}{5}$ $\frac{2}{3}$ $\frac{3}{16}$

b. combo 1 1 $\frac{3}{5}$ $\frac{1}{2}$

c. combo 3 $\frac{1}{40}$ 0 $\frac{3}{4}$

⑤

> *According to the weather report, most of the days in March last year were snowy, some of the days were cloudy, and just a few days were sunny.*

The probability of having

a. a sunny day in March next year $\frac{2}{15}$ 0 $\frac{4}{5}$

b. a snowy day in March next year 1 $\frac{2}{3}$ $\frac{1}{4}$

Think: 1:3 = 20:60

Predict the frequency of an outcome:

3 equal sections

The theoretical probability of landing on each section is $\frac{1}{3}$. If I spin the spinner 60 times, I predict that "dog" will come up about 20 times.

Find the theoretical probability and predict the frequency of each outcome.

⑥ **Draw a card from my collection without looking.**

Possible Outcomes	Probability	Prediction (Draw 50 times.)	Prediction (Draw 100 times.)
apple		about times	about times

⑦

Spin it.

Possible Outcomes	Probability	Prediction (Spin 40 times.)	Prediction (Spin 100 times.)
cat		about times	about times

Katie predicted the results of spinning each of the four spinners 100 times. Help her write each result in a fraction of the total number of spins. Then draw lines to match the predictions with the correct spinners.

⑧

Possible Outcomes	Frequency	Fraction
red	25 times	$\frac{25}{100} = \frac{1}{4}$
yellow	24 times	
green	25 times	
blue	times	

Possible Outcomes	Frequency	Fraction
red	16 times	
yellow	times	
green	50 times	

Possible Outcomes	Frequency	Fraction
red	48 times	
yellow	36 times	
green	times	

Possible Outcomes	Frequency	Fraction
red	times	
yellow	19 times	
green	18 times	
blue	20 times	

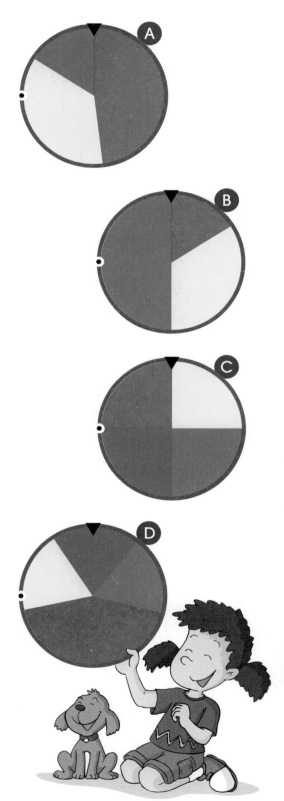

ENGLISH

Would you like to go on *safari*? The word means "journey" in Swahili, the language of east Africa. This word was later borrowed by wealthy travellers from Europe years ago, who liked going to Africa to hunt the animals there. Over time, the word *safari* became part of the English language and the term "Big Five" came about. It refers to the five most dangerous animals to hunt on safari.

So, what are the "Big Five"? The answer may surprise you.

The Big Five
of the Safari

Elephants
They are big animals, weighing up to 6000 kilograms. But they can reach a speed of up to 40 kilometres per hour. Although they have poor eyesight, they must always be approached with caution.

Rhinoceros
These animals can be as heavy as 1000 kg. They are shy and like to be left alone. If you bother them, they can get really grumpy and unpredictable. Rhinos cannot see well, but they have excellent hearing and a good sense of smell.

Leopards
At 80 kg, leopards are smaller than lions, but they make up for this with their fierceness, strength, and intelligence. Leopards can leap three metres in the air, and can carry animals that weigh three times more than they do! They have a keen sense of smell and hearing, and can see well in the dark. They like to wander alone, most often at night.

Lions
These are the largest carnivores in Africa. A male lion can weigh up to 250 kg, and its loud roar can be heard as far as 10 km away. This is why we call the lion the "King of the Beasts". Unlike leopards, lions like to spend their days sleeping with their "pride", or group, when they are not looking for food.

Water Buffalo
These are considered the most dangerous of all African animals. They are intelligent and cunning, and will band together to fight their enemy and protect the weaker members of their group. They can weigh up to 600 kg.

Fortunately, when we talk about going on safari these days, we mean we are going to visit Africa to look at the lovely beasts of the continent. We shoot them only with our cameras. And let's not forget the other amazing animals of Africa, such as the giraffe, the hippopotamus, and the wildebeest, among many, many others. Can you think of a few more?

A. Draw lines to match the descriptions with the animals.

1. leopards •   • sleep with their "pride"

2. elephants •   • can get rather grumpy and unpredictable

3. water buffalo •   • must always be approached with caution

4. rhinoceros •   • like to wander alone at night

5. lions •   • the most dangerous of all African animals

B. Order the "Big Five" by weight from the heaviest to the lightest. Write 1 to 5.

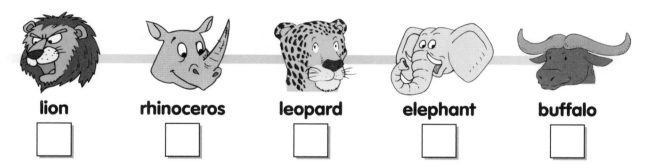

| **lion** | **rhinoceros** | **leopard** | **elephant** | **buffalo** |
| □ | □ | □ | □ | □ |

C. Give one-word answers to these questions.

1. Which word means "meat-eaters"?   _____

2. What is another word for "animals"?   _____

3. What is another word for "sharp"?   _____

4. What is the opposite of "lent"?   _____

5. Which language does the word "safari" come from?   _____

6. What does "safari" mean in its original language?   _____

Nouns (1)

Nouns can be common or proper. **Common nouns** name any people, places, things, animals, or ideas. **Proper nouns** name specific people, places, things, animals, or ideas, and always begin with a capital letter.

Examples: lady, garden, bicycle, chipmunk, happiness (common)
David, Yukon, Popsicle, Kim the Koala, Canadianism (proper)

D. Circle the common nouns and underline the proper nouns.

1.	elephants	Africa	wander	Antarctica
2.	English	safari	Big Five	well-known
3.	continent	Bernie	intelligent	the Mediterranean Sea
4.	Swahili	speed	Marie	King of the Beasts
5.	travellers	Mr. Ross	fierceness	Egyptians

E. Fill in the blanks with common or proper nouns.

1. The seven continents are North America, South America, Antarctica, Australia, Asia, Africa, and _____ .

2. As soon as he comes home from school, Amir can tell that his mother is cutting green peppers in the kitchen. As always, he has a very good _____ of smell.

3. Because I'm from Canada, I don't speak British English or American English, but _____ .

4. Sandra says, "I've gained so much weight in the past year that I am now 52 _____ ."

Nouns (2)

Nouns can be concrete or abstract. **Concrete nouns** can be recognized by our five senses (sight, hearing, smell, taste, touch). **Abstract nouns** name things such as ideas, concepts, qualities, and ideals.

Examples: colour, music, scent, sugar, paper (concrete)
thought, love, kindness, perfection (abstract)

F. Read these sentences and look at the underlined nouns. Write "C" for concrete nouns and "A" for abstract nouns.

1. Mr. Fleming always gets up before <u>sunrise</u>. _____

2. It is never too late to show some <u>generosity</u>! _____

3. "What you are looking at is <u>German Expressionism</u>," Mr. Fleming introduces his students to a style of art. _____

4. "<u>Beauty</u> is very hard to define," says Mr. Fleming. _____

5. Alan has such a good ear that he remembers every <u>song</u> in its original key. _____

6. <u>Contentment</u> is a state of mind. _____

G. Use two concrete nouns and two abstract nouns to write sentences.

1. _____

_____

2. _____

_____

3. _____

_____

4. _____

_____

Nkosi was born in South Africa on February 4, 1989. He never knew his father, and his mother had a terrible illness: her body had a virus called HIV, which often leads to AIDS. When she was pregnant with Nkosi, he became infected with the virus too. At that time, in South Africa, more than 70 000 babies were born with HIV every year, and half the people under the age of 15 would die of AIDS over the next 10 years.

There is no cure for AIDS. Babies that are born infected usually do not live longer than two years in South Africa. But Nkosi was strong. Sadly though, when he was two years old, Nkosi's mother had to take him to an AIDS care centre because she was too sick to care for him herself. A volunteer worker named Gail Johnson asked Nkosi's mother if she could become Nkosi's foster mother. She agreed and Nkosi became Gail's foster son. Together, Gail and her friends started a new AIDS care centre for children. They called it Nkosi's Haven.

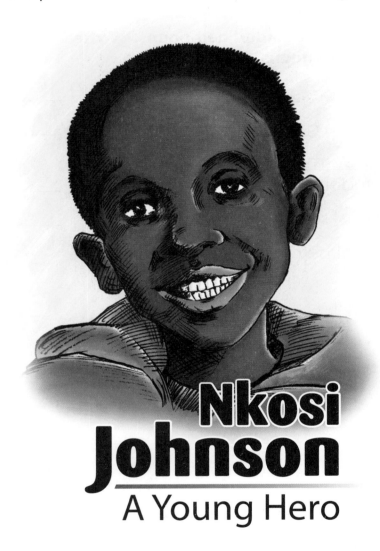

Nkosi Johnson
A Young Hero

In 1997, Nkosi's biological mother died of an AIDS-related illness. Even during this trying time, Nkosi was fighting another battle of his own. Nkosi and his foster mother wanted him to go to school, but some of the parents did not want him there because he had HIV. Gail Johnson began to talk to the public about the problem, and eventually, Nkosi was allowed to go to school. After this happened, Nkosi Johnson became a hero. He began to travel and give speeches, helping others understand HIV and not be afraid of people who had AIDS.

As Nkosi spoke for people living with AIDS, he often said these words:

"Care for us and accept us – we are all human beings...We are normal. We have hands. We have feet. We can walk, we talk, we have needs just like everyone else. Don't be afraid of us. We are all the same!"

In 2001, Nkosi Johnson died of AIDS. He was 12 years old.

A. **Read the clues and complete the word puzzle. Then finish what Amy says with the letters in the green boxes.**

1. The passage is about a brave boy named Nkosi _____ .
2. Nkosi was a _____ hero.
3. Gail Johnson was Nkosi's _____ _____ .
4. Nkosi was born in _____ _____ in 1989.
5. Nkosi got the HIV virus when his mother was _____ with him.
6. Usually, _____ born with HIV in South Africa would not have lived more than two years.
7. Nkosi's Haven is an _____ _____ _____ .
8. At first, Nkosi was not allowed to go to school because he had _____ .
9. Although Nkosi was born with HIV, he was a _____ baby.
10. At the time of his mother's death, Nkosi was _____ his own battle.
11. To help others understand HIV and AIDS, Nkosi gave _____ .

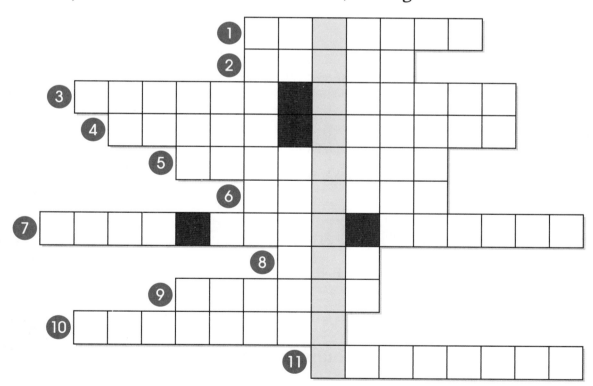

We should care for and accept one another because we are all _____ .

Adjectives (1)

An **adjective** describes a noun. It may be placed close to the noun it describes, or placed later in the sentence. Sometimes, a noun can function as an adjective.

Examples: Elizabeth is a very <u>active</u> girl.
Elizabeth is very <u>happy</u> about her party.
Elizabeth makes her own <u>party</u> costumes.

B. **Circle the adjectives and write the nouns that they describe. Then finish what Joey says.**

1. The mother was too sick to care for her son.   _____

2. Nkosi's Haven is a care centre.   _____

3. Nkosi's biological mother died of an
    AIDS-related illness.   _____ _____

4. Gail Johnson, Nkosi's foster mother, is a
    volunteer worker.   _____ _____

5. Remember that we are all human beings.
    Acceptance would then be very easy.   _____ _____

6.

> In the sentences above, the words _____ and _____ are nouns that function as adjectives.

C. **Write three sentences using nouns as adjectives.**

1. _____

2. _____

3. _____

Adjectives (2)

There are **adjectives** that show ownership: my, our, your, their, his, her, its. These are called **possessive adjectives**.

Example: Alan is riding <u>his</u> bicycle.

D. **Fill in the blanks with the correct possessive adjectives.**

The show is about to start, but Lola is still fidgeting in 1._____ seat. She is worried that her puppy will be scared, since tonight is 2._____ first time being home alone. Lola's parents tell her, "3._____ puppy will be fine. The show is not long and we'll be home in a few hours." Lola's brother Jason also tells her to enjoy the show, since he is sure that the puppy is enjoying 4._____ treats. Jason had given the puppy some cookies before heading out. He bought them from 5._____ buddy's pet store just two days ago. Still not assured, Lola tries to convince herself by thinking, "Tonight is the first time this year that we're seeing a musical in 6._____ favourite theatre. I should enjoy this evening just like the rest of 7._____ family." The only thing is, Lola wishes that the newest and tiniest member of 8._____ family were there as well.

E. **Write a paragraph using three different possessive adjectives.**

_____

_____

_____

_____

_____

Moms and dads wear wide smiles on Mother's Day and Father's Day, not only because they get colourful homemade cards, but also because there is a good chance they will be asked a question they know they will hear, "Why isn't there a Children's Day?" Of course, this question is usually followed by the answer, "But *every* day is Children's Day!"

Did you know that there really is a Children's Day? In 1993, the Government of Canada enacted Bill C-371 (a "bill" is a document that becomes law if it passes by votes in Parliament). This bill, called the Child Day Act, designated November 20 as National Child Day. This was done as a way to promote awareness of the United Nations Convention on the Rights of the Child, which was ratified in 1991.

What are rights? Perhaps you have heard of "human rights", "animal rights", or the "right to life". A "human right" is something that each person deserves to have. You do not have to earn it or work for it. It is yours simply because you exist. But not everyone agrees on what things should be considered human rights. In Canada, for example, we believe that we have the right to say what we wish to say; we have freedom of expression. But this is not the case in every country.

Did you know that years and years ago, children did not have as many rights as they do today? Children were not adults, and so it was acceptable to treat them with less respect and fairness. In some places, such as England during the Industrial Revolution, child workers were sometimes even forced to work under more unfair conditions than their adult counterparts.

According to the United Nations Convention on the Rights of the Child, children around the world have the right to the following:

- an education
- food and shelter
- special care if they have special needs
- a name and a nation
- play and rest
- health care
- special protection
- celebrations of their own culture

A. Use your dictionary to find the definitions of these words. Then use them in sentences of your own.

1. respect: _____

_____

2. awareness: _____

_____

3. document: _____

_____

4. promote: _____

_____

5. ratified: _____

_____

B. Give your opinions.

1. Why do you think "every day is Children's Day"?

_____

2. What do you think were the unfair conditions of the child workers during the Industrial Revolution in England?

_____

_____

3. Are there certain things that we should never say, even though we all have freedom of expression? Explain.

_____

_____

Verbs (1)

A **verb** is for expressing action. It can be **transitive** (must take an object) or **intransitive** (does not need an object).

Examples: Lisa <u>reads</u> a book every month. (transitive)
My little budgie <u>sings</u> when everyone is asleep. (intransitive)

C. **Write "T" for "transitive" or "I" for "intransitive" for each underlined verb. Then write the object of each transitive verb.**

1. Moms and dads <u>wear</u> smiles on Mother's Day and Father's Day.

2. "Does this camera <u>work</u>?" Tom asks his father.

3. The Government of Canada <u>enacted</u> Bill C-371 in 1993.

4. Bill C-371 <u>designated</u> November 20 as National Child Day.

5. We all <u>have</u> rights as individuals.

6. National Child Day is there to <u>promote</u> awareness of the rights of the child.

7. Alex works on the project while his cat <u>naps</u> beside him.

D. **Think of two verbs and use them in separate sentences. Then indicate whether they are transitive (T) or intransitive (I).**

1. _____

    _____

2. _____

    _____

Verbs (2)

There are **verbs** that are used along with main verbs to express things such as emphasis, ability, probability, and necessity. They are called **helping verbs**, or **auxiliary verbs**.

Examples: I <u>do</u> like this skirt! (emphasis)
Veronica <u>can</u> bake delicious cakes. (ability)
There <u>may</u> be a storm tomorrow. (probability)
I <u>have to</u> finish this project today! (necessity)

E. Circle the correct helping verb in each sentence.

1. There may / can be five millimetres of rain tomorrow, according to the weather forecast.

2. Can / May you play badminton with me?

3. Alex does / has to make a beeline to class because he is late.

4. Sheila did / may give you her phone number, didn't she?

5. My grandpa may / can keep a very beautiful garden.

6. Felicity thinks there may / can be a surprise quiz on Monday.

7. The children can / do enjoy themselves in the swimming pool!

8. " Do / May you have a wonderful year ahead," Karen wrote to her friend overseas.

F. Think of a friend's name. Use it to start two separate sentences with "do" and "can" as helping verbs. What do you notice?

1. _____

2. _____

I notice that _____

_____ .

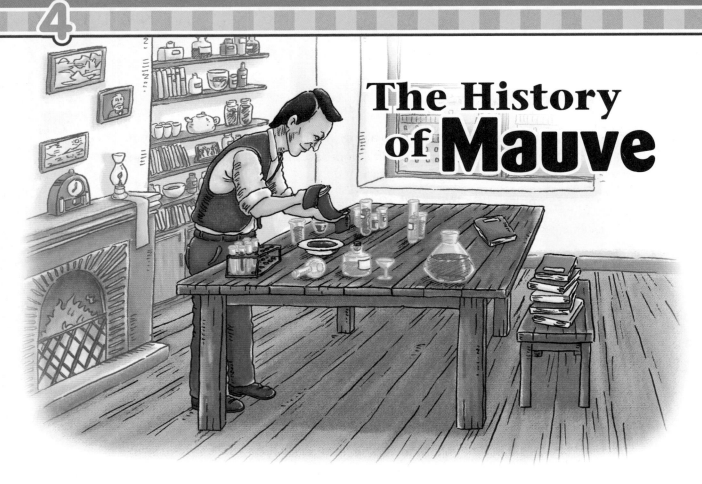

The History of Mauve

Who would have thought that a colour could have such an interesting backstory? But it is true: whether or not you like the purplish, pastel shade called "mauve", it has the most interesting history of all the colours. You could say that mauve changed the world!

As you know, mauve is not a primary colour – it is not even a secondary colour. Years ago, colours, whether in dyes or paints, were made from natural ingredients. The most common way of creating purple was from the mucus of molluscs! It was a labour-intensive process that made this colour very expensive to produce. As a result, throughout history the colour purple was always associated with royalty, because only royalty and other wealthy people could afford to buy clothes in this colour.

But all this changed in the mid-19th century with the discovery of a way to make artificial purple dye, to the credit of a man named William Henry Perkin. William was a clever student born in London, with an interest in chemistry. By the age of 15, he was already studying at the Royal College of Chemistry in London. A few years later, William worked on a way to create artificial quinine. At the time, quinine was a valuable substance used for the prevention of a disease called malaria. One day in 1856, while his boss was on holiday, William was experimenting in his own apartment "laboratory". Then something interesting happened: as he was working with a chemical mixture, a residue that had a lovely purple colour was created. William had created the first aniline dye, which he named *mauveine*.

William patented his discovery and soon many colours were being produced artificially. From that point on, synthetic dyes meant that colourful and colourfast materials could be made affordably. William became a wealthy man – and the world became a more colourful place.

A. Circle the correct answers.

1. Which word means "history" or "background"?
    A. royalty   B. backstory   C. ingredients

2. The disease that could be prevented by quinine is _____ .
    A. malaria   B. molluscs   C. mauveine

3. If something is dyed in colours that will not easily fade, it is _____ .
    A. purple   B. colourful   C. colourfast

4. When something is human-made, it is _____ .
    A. chemical   B. patented   C. artificial

5. Another word for "artificial" is _____ .
    A. residue   B. synthetic   C. mixture

B. Fill in the blanks with words beginning with "p" in the passage.

1. Red, yellow, and blue are the three _____ colours from which other colours can be created.

2. Sara shows her brother a piece of paper smeared with different shades of pink and says, "I made this masterpiece with my box of _____ crayons!"

3. The _____ of making a painting consists of multiple steps, from making sketches to applying varnish, which is a transparent coating that protects the work.

4. "A lot of the work that health researchers are doing right now is for the _____ of disease outbreaks," says Dr. Stein, who is a guest speaker at our school assembly.

5. Lavender and mauve are both _____ , elegant shades.

6. "How many pieces of work do you _____ in a year?" Michael asks Andrea, who is a professional painter.

Adverbs

An **adverb** describes a verb. It can also describe an adjective or another adverb.

Examples: The lady laughed <u>heartily</u>.
My cousin likes <u>very</u> pale colours.
Calvin did his math test <u>pretty</u> well.

C. Fill in the blanks with the correct adverbs.

> almost   any   too   fully   soundly   hard
> rather   really   partly   usually

1. "You're only _____ right, so I'm not going to agree with you," says Felix to Jessie.

2. "Having made a quick decision does not necessarily mean you have made it _____ ," Dad tells Vickie.

3. "I'd _____ try the cherry cheesecake than the raspberry pie," Mom tells Jessie.

4. "I've changed your room from an ugly green to a lovely mauve," says Vickie to her sister. "Is it _____ better yet?"

5. "Felix, you cleaned your plate _____ fast. Feel free to have a second helping of that salad," Mom says.

6. "Mom," Jessie says, "we cook the same things a little _____ often. Should we try something new?"

7. "What you said made a lot of sense. I _____ agree with you," Dad tells a friend.

8. "Dinner is _____ ready!" Mom calls out from the kitchen.

D. Underline the adverbs in these paragraphs.

1. Before mauve could be artificially produced, the most common way of creating purple was from the mucus of molluscs, which was a difficult process that made the colour very expensive. This is why purple is historically linked with royalty and the wealthy.

2. It was William Henry Perkin who substantially changed the value of purple when he discovered a way to make artificial purple dye. As a bright, young student, William was already studying at the Royal College of Chemistry in London by the age of 15. A few years later, he was actually trying to make artificial quinine in his own apartment when he accidentally created a lovely purple colour.

3. It is really fascinating that so many things can be created by accident. Imagine what our world would be missing if no one bothered trying to make anything. If it were not for someone like William Perkin who was working hard as a scientist, the beautiful purple dye might still not be affordably made today.

E. Read each pair of sentences carefully. Underline the adverb and circle the adjective. Then answer Ben's question.

1. You're a fast walker. Do you walk this fast all the time?

2. Keri was the first one to finish. She gets to go first in the next round.

3. This is a far cry from what I ever expected of you! It seems like you will go very far in architecture.

4.

> *What do you notice about each pair of sentences?*

_____

_____

THE GROUP OF SEVEN

What is the Group of Seven? Is it an alliance of countries? Is it a rock band? It is actually a group of Canadian painters that is just as famous in the Canadian art circles as any Juno Award-winning rock star.

In 1920, J.E.H. MacDonald, A.Y. Jackson, Arthur Lismer, Franklin Carmichael, Lawren Harris, F.H. Varley, and Frank Johnston formed a club. These men were all painters who were drawn to the rugged landscape of the Canadian Shield – the vast stretch of ancient rock around Hudson Bay that blankets much of eastern and central Canada in a horseshoe shape. Their colourful and impressionistic depictions of the rocks, trees, and lakes of this landscape were infused with spirit and power, giving their work a unique and innovative style. In the beginning, critics scoffed at their work. Now, however, their paintings – as well as those of Tom Thomson, who died before the group was formed – are some of the world's highly prized Canadian art.

For these artists, the rugged country inspired them not only with respect to their paintings, but also with respect to life. They developed a set of principles, or sentiments that they called "algomaxims", which is a reference to Algonquin Park, where they often worked. Even today, decades later, it is interesting to see how these sentiments reflect the collective nature of Canadians.

- The great purpose of landscape art is to make us at home in our own country.
- Get in the habit of looking at the sky. It is the source of light and art.
- Canada consists of 3 500 523 square miles of mostly landscape. It is apparently intended to be the home of broadminded people.
- A critic is known by the company he keeps.
- Coordinate your ideas so that you are advanced by all of them.
- The more you know, the less you condemn.
- The blue glasses of Prejudice spoil all colour schemes.

A. **Circle "T" for the true sentences and "F" for the false ones.**

1. The Group of Seven was a group of Canadian painters.　　T　F

2. Arthur Lismer and A.Y. Jackson painted scenes of the Arctic Lands.　　T　F

3. The Canadian Shield has a rugged landscape that attracted the Group of Seven.　　T　F

4. Tom Thomson was also an impressionistic painter.　　T　F

5. The Canadian Shield covers much of the country's northern wilderness in a horseshoe shape.　　T　F

B. **Quote one or two sentences from the passage to support each of the following.**

1. At the start of the Group of Seven's career, their paintings were not valued at all.

   _____

   _____

2. The Canadian Shield influenced both the Group of Seven's work and their approach to life.

   _____

   _____

3. A vast, open environment is connected to an openness of mind.

   _____

   _____

4. Knowledge breeds acceptance.

   _____

   _____

Agreement

In a sentence, the words must **agree** in person and number.

Examples: Julie always <u>forgets</u> to bring <u>her</u> homework to school.
Julie and Tom <u>are</u> celebrating <u>their</u> 12th birthday.
Julie and Tom <u>know</u> that their mother has baked <u>them</u> a cake.

C. Circle the correct words to make agreement.

1. Canadian painters like A.Y. Jackson and Arthur Lismer was / were greatly inspired by the landscape of the Canadian Shield.

2. The paintings of the Group of Seven portray / portrays Canada as a land of colour, giving it / them spirit and power.

3. Kevin is / are using the paintings of Tom Thomson as his / their learning tools in art class.

4. The more Sheila uses its / her new brush, the more she get / gets used to it.

5. Sheila knows that Kevin is / are an indoor person, but she hopes he will listen to him / her and go out to get some fresh air.

6. Kevin look / looks at the photographs taken by Mom and exclaims, " These / This are such pretty photos of Vancouver!"

7. Mom points to a picture of the Rockies and says, "I'm going to frame that / those one over there. It's the first picture I took with my / its new camera."

D. Read and rewrite these sentences to make them agree.

1. "If critics are known by the company he keep, are we then known by the friends we have?" Julie asks her dad.

    _____

    _____

2. Whatever you decides to do, make sure you are brave enough to confront the unexpected.

    _____

    _____

3. When we says, "A rose by any other name will smell as sweet", we are saying that something will still be the same even if we give them a different name.

    _____

    _____

    _____

E. Start sentences with the following words. Make sure there is agreement.

1. Kimberly _____

    _____ .

2. The kids at the park _____

    _____ .

3. The school _____

    _____ .

4. Mom and Dad _____

    _____ .

Planet "Chanyikhei"

When Chan Yik Hei was seven years old, he saw a television show about a robot. This was the start of his love of science, especially of robots. At the age of 15, Yik Hei became an award-winning inventor. In 2004 at the 55th Intel International Science and Engineering Fair in Portland, United States, he won second place for his invention: a domestic security robot which he named "Total Equip".

The robot is about a metre high. To save money, Yik Hei made the body from a trash bin. One of the innovations about this robot, as far as house alarms go, is that it is not fixed in place, which would have made it easy for burglars to disable. Total Equip moves around the house on wheels – in this case, skateboard wheels! It is also able to notify the police or fire department if necessary, and has a built-in camera.

Yik Hei is passionate about what he does. He does not spend much time playing computer games or singing karaoke. In fact, as a high school student, Yik Hei took adult evening classes on robotics. He is a true inventor and scientist, who understands that there are always going to be setbacks along the road to his discoveries and scientific creations. If you went to his home, you would see some of his "failed" experiments. He would tell you that these "failures" were in fact his learning experiences. He believes that learning is its own reward, and that failure is the path to success.

With his success came a unique and surprising reward. After his second-place win at the fair, Yik Hei was amazed to learn that a planet had been named after him! His name had been put forward by Ceres Connection, a program run by the Science Services Department of the Massachusetts Institute of Technology (MIT), in recognition and appreciation of his scientific endeavours. The name was then approved by the International Committee for Small Body Nomenclature.

Planet "20780 Chanyikhei" (formerly known as "minor planet number 20780) is three to seven kilometres in diameter and is located between Jupiter and Mars. It was discovered by MIT's Near-Earth Asteroid Research Program in September, 2000. Its new name is a fitting tribute to the young scientist.

A. **Read the clues and complete the crossword puzzle with words from the passage.**

Across

A. new ideas
B. board mounted on roller skate wheels
C. obstacles
D. to do with the home or household
E. system of names used in a scientific field

Down

1. the study of robots
2. what Yik Hei considers to be his learning experiences
3. something done out of respect for a person
4. feeling strongly about something

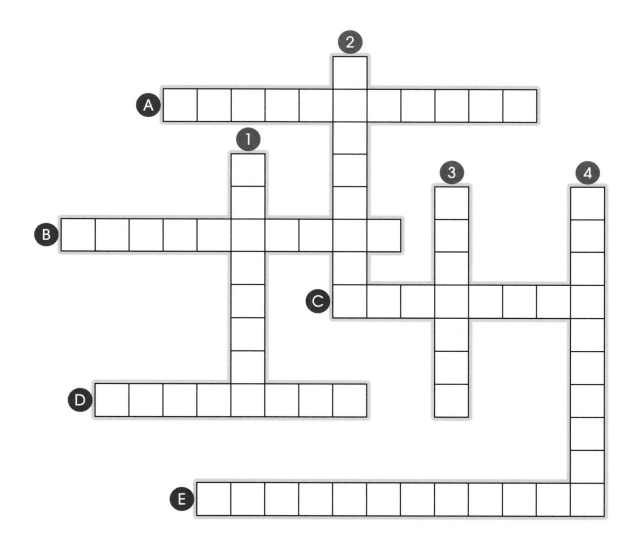

Subjects and Objects

A sentence always begins with a **subject**, which is a person or thing that performs an action. It may also contain an **object**, which is a person or thing that receives the action (direct), or a person or thing that the action is directed to (indirect).

Examples: Adrian is singing. (subject only)
 Adrian is singing a song. (subject and direct object)
 Adrian sang Dave a song. (subject and indirect object)

B. Write "subject" or "object" for the underlined words.

1. Chan Yik Hei is <u>an award-winning inventor</u>. _____

2. <u>He</u> made a domestic security robot that is about one metre high. _____

3. <u>Total Equip</u> moves easily around the house on skateboard wheels. _____

4. The robot is able to notify <u>the police</u> or fire department if necessary. _____

5. MIT recognized <u>Chan Yik Hei's scientific endeavours</u> by naming a planet after him. _____

C. Check the sentences that contain an indirect object and underline it.

1. Mr. Forrester wrote Mrs. Forrester a detailed letter about his job overseas. ☐

2. With Yik Hei's success came a surprising award. ☐

3. The students in Mrs. Forrester's class sent a needy family a box of non-perishable food for Christmas. ☐

4. Laura mailed her cousin a very cute Christmas card. ☐

5. Angelo called his best friend as soon as he was finished with his homework. ☐

D. **Fill in the blanks with subjects, direct objects, or indirect objects to complete the sentences.**

1. Each student has a chance to present _____ to the whole class.

2. _____ will be the flag-bearer for her country in this year's Winter Olympics.

3. Dad brought _____ a few nice books for pleasure reading.

4. "_____ is full of surprises whether you like it or not!" Mom tells Jessie.

5. Mr. Bourne gave Jordan _____ that he will remember for a very long time.

6. The coach urged _____ to give it their best even though the other team is winning and the game is almost over.

7. _____ are full of lights as the city prepares itself for the holiday season.

E. **Use these words as the subject in one sentence and as the object in another.**

1. Jake the Dog

   _____

   _____

2. Grandpa

   _____

   _____

3. the wilderness

   _____

   _____

Too Nice to Be Forgotten

Frankie Chu was a cool dad. He lived and worked as a busy lawyer in New York City with his wife Karen and his daughters Ariel and Petrina. One day, as Frankie was about to leave for his morning commute, the telephone rang. Frankie waited for his wife to take the call because she was going to Manhattan with him that day. As a result of the phone call, they missed their train, and Frankie was going to be late for his meeting at the World Trade Center. It was September 11, 2001.

The World Trade Center was attacked that morning by terrorists, and 3000 people died when the buildings collapsed. Frankie was deeply affected by this, and felt that he should do something more with his life. Within weeks, Frankie left his job and returned to Hong Kong with his family. He decided it was time to pursue his dream.

Frankie had long been interested in computers and in education, so he started his own educational software company, developing ways to use computer technology to improve children's thinking skills. On March 15, 2003, Frankie got on a flight to China to present the project to business people there. One of the passengers on the plane was sick with a very contagious illness called SARS (severe acute respiratory syndrome). The sickness spread to 18 other passengers, including Frankie himself. The illness had already killed many people in Hong Kong and elsewhere.

Ariel, Petrina, and their mother were scared, but they were inspired by their father's example. While their father was in hospital, Ariel and Petrina started writing him poems and drawings, calling the collection "Wishing Daddy to Come Home". Unfortunately, Frankie never came home.

Ariel and Petrina put together a book about their father, and called it *Too Nice to Be Forgotten*. After the manuscript was rejected by several local publishers, a family friend paid to have the book published and distributed. *Too Nice to Be Forgotten* went on sale in December of 2003 and, within weeks, sold out its first print run of 10 000 copies. It has been reprinted several times since. The book is not only a tribute to Frankie Chu, a cool dad, but also proof of the love and strong spirit shown by his wife and daughters in the most difficult of times.

A. Read these clues and circle the words in the word search.

· Frankie's profession in New York City
· the city where Frankie is originally from
· original draft of a piece of writing
· companies that produce books
· what Frankie was interested in besides computers
· the country where Frankie was to present his project

u	N	o	M	a	n	h	a	t	t	a	n	K	a	r	e	n
p	e	l	P	H	o	n	g	▓	K	o	n	g	j	o	b	N
r	w	a	e	y	C	b	u	s	i	n	e	s	s	C	h	e
o	▓	w	t	t	h	p	u	b	l	i	s	h	e	r	s	w
j	Y	y	r	i	i	W	o	r	l	d	▓	T	r	a	d	e
e	o	e	i	c	n	e	c	o	m	p	u	t	e	r	s	Y
c	r	r	n	m	a	n	u	s	c	r	i	p	t	A	r	o
t	e	d	u	c	a	t	i	o	n	a	C	e	n	t	e	r

B. Answer these questions.

1. What happened in Manhattan on September 11, 2001?

_____

2. How did the incident on September 11 affect Frankie? What did he do?

_____

_____

3. What is the significance of the book *Too Nice to Be Forgotten*?

_____

_____

Pronouns (1)

Pronouns are used to refer to nouns. There are many types, such as **subject pronouns**, **object pronouns** (which can be direct or indirect), **possessive pronouns**, and **reflexive pronouns**.

Examples: <u>Tom</u> went swimming. <u>He</u> went swimming. (subject)
Tom fixed <u>his lead pencil</u>. Tom fixed <u>it</u>. (direct object)
Bob asked <u>Tom</u> something. Bob asked <u>him</u> something. (indirect object)
This room is <u>Tom's</u>. This room is <u>his</u>. (possessive)
Tom can look after <u>himself</u> at camp. (reflexive)

C. **Rewrite each sentence by replacing the underlined words with a pronoun. Then write "S" for "subject", "D" for "direct object", or "I" for "indirect object".**

1. Ariel and Petrina called <u>their collection of poems and drawings</u> "Wishing Daddy to Come Home".

   _____   ☐

2. The local publishers returned the manuscript to <u>the family</u>, but the book ended up selling out its first print run.

   _____   ☐

3. <u>Frankie Chu</u> was a cool dad, living and working as a busy lawyer in one of the world's most dynamic cities.

   _____   ☐

4. Has Ella told you <u>the story about the family that pulled themselves together in spite of tragedy</u>?

   _____   ☐

D. **Underline the subject pronouns and circle the reflexive pronouns.**

Frankie decided he should pursue his dream after that fateful morning of September 11, 2001. Two years later, his new educational software company was well on its way to China when another tragedy struck, and this time Frankie became a victim himself. His daughters were scared, but were nevertheless inspired by their father's do-good example. They kept themselves strong in spirit. Their mother stayed strong herself as well. They wrote Frankie poems and made him drawings while he was in hospital. They continued to write after his death, putting together a book that was their tribute to him, selling out its first print run. Although a wife has lost her husband and two young daughters have lost their father, this family has shown us that staying strong is possible even when it seems impossible to do so.

E. **Write a paragraph using three of these possessive pronouns.**

mine   ours   yours   theirs   his   hers

_____

_____

_____

_____

_____

_____

_____

How the world is full of wonders! The CN Tower in Canada, the Taj Mahal in India, and the Victoria Falls in the heart of Africa are three of the many wonders we can see today. But some of our world's wonders no longer exist. They have become a part of history. We can only read about them and imagine their greatness.

This is where the list of the Seven Wonders of the Ancient World comes in. The list was written around 200 BCE. People liked making these types of lists even back then!

On the Euphrates River, just south of present-day Baghdad, Iraq, a Babylonian king named Nebuchadnezzar II (604 to 562 BCE) built **the Hanging Gardens of Babylon**, which had an irrigation system that lifted water *up* from the river.

The Statue of Zeus at Olympia, situated 150 kilometres west of Athens, was built to honour the Olympic Games, before it was moved to Constantinople and destroyed by fire in 462 CE.

The Temple of Artemis at Ephesus was made of marble and built around 550 BCE in present-day Turkey. In 356 BCE, it was burned to the ground by an arsonist.

The Mausoleum at Halicarnassus was also built in Turkey, in the city of Bodrum. Construction was completed in 350 BCE. By 1522, it had been taken apart by invading forces over the years.

The Seven Wonders
of the Ancient World

The Colossus of Rhodes was built at the entrance to the harbour of Rhodes in the Aegean Sea, situated between Greece and Turkey. It was partially destroyed by an earthquake around 226 BCE.

The Lighthouse of Alexandria is the only ancient wonder that had a practical use. It was built in what is now Alexandria, Egypt, around 250 BCE. Several earthquakes over the years destroyed it.

The Great Pyramid of Giza is the only ancient wonder that we can still see today! Located at the edge of Cairo, Egypt, it was built around 2560 BCE as a tomb for the Pharaoh Khufu. It is the oldest of the ancient wonders, but has outlasted the rest of them. How fortunate we are to be able to see it today!

A. **Read what Jake says and write the names of the Seven Wonders of the Ancient World.**

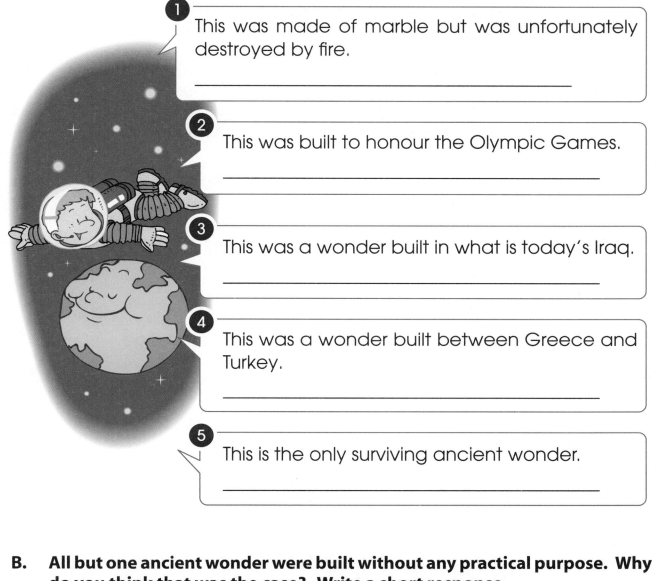

1 This was made of marble but was unfortunately destroyed by fire.

_____

2 This was built to honour the Olympic Games.

_____

3 This was a wonder built in what is today's Iraq.

_____

4 This was a wonder built between Greece and Turkey.

_____

5 This is the only surviving ancient wonder.

_____

B. **All but one ancient wonder were built without any practical purpose. Why do you think that was the case? Write a short response.**

_____

_____

_____

_____

_____

Pronouns (2)

There are other types of pronouns like **interrogative pronouns, relative pronouns**, and **reciprocal pronouns**. Many interrogative pronouns can also be relative pronouns. Some interrogative pronouns, namely "what", "which", and "whom", can be used indirectly.

Examples: <u>Whose</u> are these socks? (interrogative)
To <u>whom</u> were you referring just now? (indirect interrogative)
This is the teacher <u>who</u> told me the story. (relative)
Julie and Alana always look out for <u>each other</u>. (reciprocal)

C.   Check the correct sentences.

Check the sentence with...

1.   ...an interrogative pronoun:

   A   Who is behind the slide?

   B   Mia does not know the girl who is behind the slide.

2.   ...an interrogative pronoun:

   A   This is the pie which has raspberries in it.

   B   Which do you think is the raspberry pie?

3.   ...a relative pronoun:

   A   David is the one who can make fantastic doodles.

   B   Who can make fantastic doodles in this grade six class?

4.   ...a relative pronoun:

   A   Whose are those books scattered on the floor?

   B   Sara is the girl whose books are always scattered on the floor.

5.   ...an interrogative pronoun used indirectly:

   A   Thomas is the one who laughed at my joke.

   B   Thomas is the one to whom I was telling the joke.

D. **Fill in the blanks with the correct pronouns.**

> what   where   which   who   whose
> whom   that   each other   one another

1. The CN Tower is the structure _____ stands out from the rest of the skyline.

2. "_____ is it that you wanted to tell me about yesterday?" Maggie asks her little brother.

3. Whenever the four of us go skiing in the mountains, we always look out for _____ .

4. "_____ of you did a better job at saving up your allowance?" Mom asks Bobby and Toby.

5. There you are! You are the one _____ I've been looking for all week!

6. My parents always help _____ out when planting new flowers in the garden.

7. Nebuchadnezzar II is the Babylonian king _____ built the Hanging Gardens of Babylon.

8. "_____ is this?" Mrs. Fells waves a cute orange pencil case in front of the class.

9. The sweater _____ looks best on you is the purple one over there.

E. **See if you can use "who", "whom", and "whose" in the same sentence.**

_____

_____

_____

The Vancouver Island Marmot

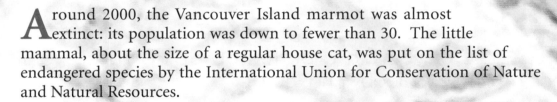

Around 2000, the Vancouver Island marmot was almost extinct: its population was down to fewer than 30. The little mammal, about the size of a regular house cat, was put on the list of endangered species by the International Union for Conservation of Nature and Natural Resources.

With chocolate brown fur and a white patch on its snout, this particular marmot species inhabits Vancouver Island and does not exist anywhere else. Its loss on Vancouver Island would consequently be a loss for the entire world. Scientists have been working hard not only to keep the marmot population from dwindling but also to raise it to an ecologically stable level. It is not clear exactly what caused the decline of the Vancouver Island marmot, but there are several possible explanations.

In order to survive, the marmot needs the kind of shelter and food that it can find only on Vancouver Island's subalpine meadows, which are located very high in the mountains. The island does not have very many of these places to begin with, so the loss of this kind of habitat is particularly hard on the marmot population. Habitat loss occurs as a result of ski resort construction, residential development, and flooding caused by nearby hydroelectric dams.

The dwindling marmot population may also be due to severe changes in weather and climate. Because marmot colonies are small, an unusually cold year could wipe out a significant number.

Clear-cutting of forests, which is a forestry practice whereby all or most of the trees in one area are cut to facilitate the growth of new ones, has a detrimental effect on marmot colonies too. The marmots move into these new open spaces because they resemble their natural habitat with large openings, flowers to eat, and good visibility. However, as the new trees grow, predators start coming as well because they can hide among the trees to prey on the marmots.

Whatever the reason for its near extinction, it is clear that we must continue to do research on the Vancouver Island marmot so that we can properly help its population recover.

A.   Fill in the blanks with words from the passage.

1.   The Vancouver Island marmot is a brown _____ with a white patch on its _____ .

2.   This marmot _____ only Vancouver Island and cannot be found anywhere else on Earth.

3.   The Vancouver Island marmot was put on the list of _____ species around 2000 because of its near _____ .

4.   The real reason for the _____ population of the Vancouver Island marmot is still unknown.

5.   Scientists have been trying to raise the marmot population to an _____ stable level.

6.   _____ on this marmot species can help recover its population.

B.   In no more than 60 words, write the possible reasons for the decline in the Vancouver Island marmot population.

_____

_____

_____

_____

_____

_____

_____

The Present Tense

We use the **simple present tense** to talk about a habit or a simple truth. We can also use it to introduce a quotation. We use the **present progressive tense** to talk about something that is going on, or something that is planned for the future.

Examples: Alana <u>goes</u> to church every Sunday.
The newspaper <u>says</u> "fewer people go to church now".
Alana <u>is playing</u> the organ right now.
Alana <u>is going</u> to church again next Sunday.

C.   Check the correct sentences. Put a cross for the wrong ones and rewrite them.

1   The Vancouver Island marmot is about the size of a regular house cat.

_____

2   The sand dollar lives in the Atlantic Ocean and the Pacific Ocean.

_____

_____

3   The clear-cut forest is resembling the natural habitat of marmots.

_____

_____

4   There is one part of his speech that says, "Ask not what your country can do for you. Ask what you can do for your country."

_____

_____

5   The magazine article is explaining, "Climate change is already affecting the polar bear population in the Arctic."

_____

_____

D.   Use each verb in the present progressive tense.

1.   inhabit   _____

_____

2.   exist   _____

_____

3.   dwindle   _____

_____

4.   raise   _____

_____

5.   cause   _____

_____

E.   Use each verb in the present progressive tense.

1.   survive   _____

_____

2.   wipe   _____

_____

3.   facilitate   _____

_____

4.   prey   _____

_____

5.   recover   _____

_____

The Governor General's
Bravery Awards

Did you know that there is a system for honouring brave people in Canada? The Decorations for Bravery were created by Queen Elizabeth II in 1972. Since then, these awards have been presented by the governor general to ordinary people who have shown extraordinary courage. Anyone can submit the name of a person who has risked injury or death to save another person. A Canadian must have been involved in the incident, although the person nominated does not need to be Canadian, and the incident need not have happened in Canada.

There are three different decorations for bravery. The Medal of Bravery is awarded for "acts of bravery in hazardous circumstances". The Star of Courage is awarded for "acts of conspicuous courage in circumstances of great peril". The Cross of Valour is awarded for "acts of the most conspicuous courage in circumstances of extreme peril". These decorations are sometimes awarded posthumously. In fact, many of the recipients of these bravery awards died saving others. People who have been awarded these decorations for bravery are entitled to put the letters M.B., S.C., and C.V. after their names. We call these "post-nominal letters".

The stories of these brave people are remarkable. For example, Mrs. Anna Ruth Lang, C.V., from Nauwigewauk, New Brunswick, saved two people from drowning after her car was hit by a fuel tanker and pushed through a bridge barrier into the Hammond River. The tanker also fell into the river and exploded, covering the water with flames. Mrs. Lang was able to swim out of her car to shore, but then removed her heavy clothing and returned to her submerged car to save her passengers. In saving their lives, she received extensive burns.

There are very young recipients as well. One of the youngest is Miss Jocelyn McDonald, S.C., of Minaki, Ontario. In 1992, when she was seven years old, Jocelyn prevented her five-year-old friend from being attacked. Other recipients are Miss Tara Benn, M.B. and Miss Tammy Benn, M.B., fourteen-year-old twin sisters from Woodville, Ontario, who received their decorations when they apprehended a gang member that was armed with a knife, preventing him from attacking a young man.

A. Read the clues and complete the crossword puzzle with words from the passage.

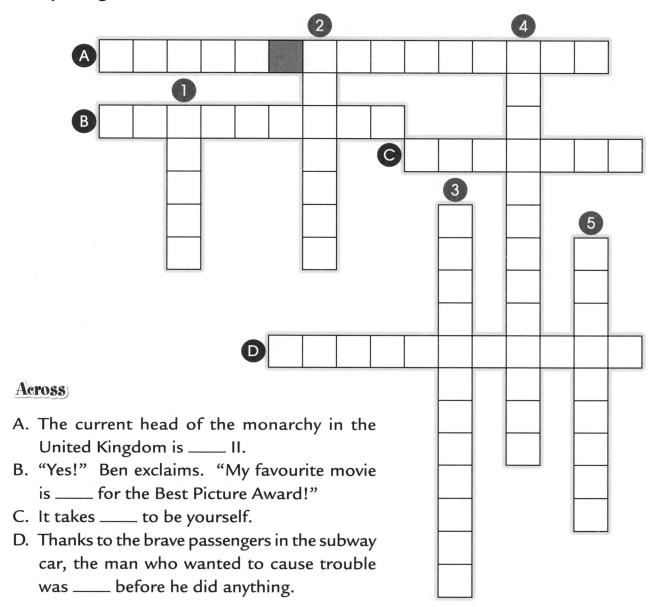

Across

A. The current head of the monarchy in the United Kingdom is _____ II.

B. "Yes!" Ben exclaims. "My favourite movie is _____ for the Best Picture Award!"

C. It takes _____ to be yourself.

D. Thanks to the brave passengers in the subway car, the man who wanted to cause trouble was _____ before he did anything.

Down

1. Dorothy is aiming for an Olympic _____ for the snowboarding event.

2. Some people live in _____ poverty and every bit of help counts.

3. Honouring someone _____ does not make the award less significant.

4. It is remarkable how ordinary people can do _____ things.

5. My music teacher has _____ knowledge of the Baroque period.

The Past Tense

We use the **simple past tense** to talk about something that happened habitually or at a particular time in the past. We can also use the simple past tense to speak politely. We use the **past progressive tense** to talk about something that continued to happen before and after a particular time in the past.

Examples: Alana <u>went</u> to church for three years.
Alana <u>mailed</u> her best friend a letter this morning.
<u>Could</u> you repeat the question, please?
Alana <u>was walking</u> home when she saw her dad.

B. **Choose the correct verbs for the sentences and use them in the simple past tense or the past progressive tense.**

talk	spread	grind	cut	strike
lie	watch	do	storm	run

1. After school, Alana _____ to her volleyball practice.

2. Mom _____ onion slices in the kitchen when Dad _____ into the house with take-out Chinese food.

3. "_____ you want to talk to me about something?" Mrs. Stephanoff asked Lisa.

4. Dad _____ some very dark coffee beans this morning.

5. I know that my little sister _____ when she said she _____ only an hour of TV.

6. Cinderella _____ with the prince when the clock _____ midnight.

7. For breakfast this morning, Brianna _____ some Nutella on her toast.

C. **Fill in the blanks with the simple past tense or the past progressive tense of the given verbs.**

It was one lovely winter morning. Though the air was cold, it was comforting nonetheless. Josephine and her little sister Amy (decide) 1._____ to head out to the frozen lake in the woods. Before they (go) 2._____ out of the house, the two of them made sure to take their skates: Josephine (choose) 3._____ her favourite black pair while Amy (bring) 4._____ out her shiny new pink ones. They (skate) 5._____ happily when all of a sudden, Amy (fall) 6._____ through a crack in the ice. Panicking, Josephine (rush) 7._____ to Amy and tried to pull her out. Both of them (gasp) 8._____ because they (lose) 9._____ energy. Then they (hear) 10._____ a familiar voice in the distance: "Josephine, Amy, it's time to go home!" It was their father. He (come) 11._____ out to fetch the two skaters. Fortunately, it was not long before he and Josephine (pull) 12._____ Amy out of the chilling water. Having always taken her family for granted, Amy (realize) 13._____ that day that she should be nicer to her family, and was even politer than usual at the dinner table. Instead of grabbing whatever she (want) 14._____, she asked, "Dad, (can) 15._____ you please pass the salad?"

Necessity *Is the Mother of* Invention

Canadians are an inventive bunch, and it should come as no surprise. In the past, Canada was not an easy place to live at all, being a vast country with relatively few people, so Canadians needed a great amount of ingenuity simply to survive each day. From early on, it was necessary to think of ways to communicate and travel quickly, and over long distances.

It is not surprising then, that one of Canada's most famous inventors is Alexander Graham Bell, who invented the telephone in 1876. He was born in Scotland, but spent much of his life in Canada. The world's first "long distance" phone call was made on August 4, 1876 from Bell's home in Brantford to Paris, Ontario, a couple of miles away. About half a century later in 1942, another Canadian named Donald Hings invented the "walkie-talkie", a form of wireless communication. In 1994, James Gosling invented Java script, the language of computer programming, which helped to make communication possible in yet another form.

Alexander Graham Bell also co-invented the hydrofoil boat with Casey Baldwin in 1908, and was a pioneer in early aviation design. And it is not surprising to learn that the snowmobile was invented in 1922 by Joseph-Armand Bombardier of Quebec. The snow blower was invented five years later by another Quebecer named Arthur Sicard.

Canada is also a world leader in the electricity generation, and in the manufacturing of electric goods. Canadians James Woodward and Matthew Evans invented the electric light bulb in 1874, later selling the patent to Thomas Edison. Soon, other Canadians began inventing things that ran on electricity, like the electric streetcar, invented by John Joseph Wright in 1883; the electric organ, patented by Morse Robb of Belleville, Ontario, in 1928; the electric wheelchair, created in 1954 by George Klein as a way to help disabled WWII veterans; and the electronic automated postal sorter, invented by Maurice Levy in 1957.

From the jetliner designed in 1949 by James Floyd to the Jolly Jumper invented in 1959 by Olivia Poole, as well as the paint roller, the lawn sprinkler, and many more, Canadians have ingeniously found ways to make life a little easier and a little more fun for everyone.

A. **Circle the correct answers.**

1. In the past, Canadians needed ingenuity to survive because _____ .

   A. Canada was a huge country with too many people
   B. Canada was a huge country with very few people
   C. Canada was a tiny country with too few people

2. Both the "walkie-talkie" and Java script are _____ .

   A. ways of travel over long distances
   B. forms of communication
   C. cellular phones

3. The inventor of the telephone was _____ .

   A. Baldwin   B. Edison   C. Bell

4. Both the snowmobile and the snow blower were invented in _____ .

   A. Ontario   B. Alberta   C. Quebec

5. The _____ was invented to help WWII veterans.

   A. light bulb   B. streetcar   C. electric wheelchair

B. **Read what Clara says and write a short response.**

> *Is necessity really the mother of invention? Why or why not? Without necessity, do you think we would still invent things? Explain and give examples.*

_____

_____

_____

_____

_____

The Future Tense

We use the **simple future tense** to talk about something that will happen. We also use it to talk about cause and effect. We use the **future progressive tense** to talk about something that will happen over a period of time.

Examples: Lisa <u>will perform</u> her new song tonight.
If you drop this, it <u>will break</u>.
Lisa <u>will be touring</u> the rest of Canada this summer.

C. Read what these inventors say. Circle the correct future tense.

1. Bell: The telephone will become / will be becoming an indispensible device for people worldwide!

2. Sicard: This snow blower will save / will be saving lots of time for people living in this snowy country!

3. Wright: The streetcar is such an environmentally friendly form of transportation that Canadians will use / will be using it for many, many years.

4. Klein: This electric wheelchair will help / will be helping disabled war veterans throughout their lifetime.

5. Gosling: My Java script will bring / will be bringing communication to a whole new level.

D. Rewrite each sentence.

1. "Don't worry," says Kim. "The rain will be stopping. I know it will."

_____

2. I'm putting this letter on top so that she will be reading it first.

_____

3. I'm sure Wendy will be staying at home and will draw holiday cards for her friends all afternoon.

_____

_____

4. Now that we are able to communicate wirelessly, he will be preferring to send me an e-mail instead of a handwritten letter.

_____

_____

5. If you use your diaphragm properly, you will breathe better and will be singing better too.

_____

_____

6. When it is colder, the air will clear and the haze will be disappearing.

_____

_____

E.   Think about your own future. Write a sentence about each of the following.

1. Something that will happen over a period of time:

_____

_____

2. Something that will happen, with no definite period of time:

_____

_____

3. Something that will happen as a result of something else:

_____

_____

He Called Me "Potato Head"!

"Why are you looking so sad, Patrick?" asked the old man.

The little boy looked up at his grandfather. "Today at school, Shane McGuire called me a potato head!"

The old man's eyes smiled down at the boy. "Is that all?" Grandpa chuckled. "Well, if that young man knew anything about potatoes, he'd know that he just paid you a compliment."

"What do you mean?" his grandson asked.

"The potato, my boy, is one of the most loved vegetables in the world. Where would we all be without the potato? It's hearty, adaptable, delicious, satisfying, and very good for you!"

Patrick laughed. "What else do you know about potatoes, Gramps?"

"That's the spirit, my boy! Well, let me see...The potato was first grown in South America. It was tough and durable, growing on the hillsides of the Andes Mountain range. Farmers there have been growing potatoes for more than 7000 years! It wasn't until the 16th century that the Spanish conquistadors entered what is now Peru, and brought the potato back to Europe with them. Still, it was another 200 years before potatoes were grown widely in Ireland. We soon learned that we could feed ten people with just an acre of potatoes. We started growing them all over Ireland and the population of our country exploded. Sad to say, though, when the potatoes were infected with a fungus in the 1840s, there was a terrible famine. The population of Ireland was cut in half by starvation and by emigration, mostly to North America. But we Irish took our love of the potato with us, and it caught on there, too. Now, Canadians and Americans love potatoes as well."

"So, Paddy," Grandpa continued, "the next time that Shane McGuire says you're a potato head, just tell him there's nothing wrong with potatoes. But there's definitely something wrong with bullies who think it's okay to call people names."

A. **Read the clues and complete the crossword puzzle with words from the passage.**

Across

A. the people who brought the potato to Europe
B. where potatoes were first grown
C. a measure of land
D. extreme food shortage

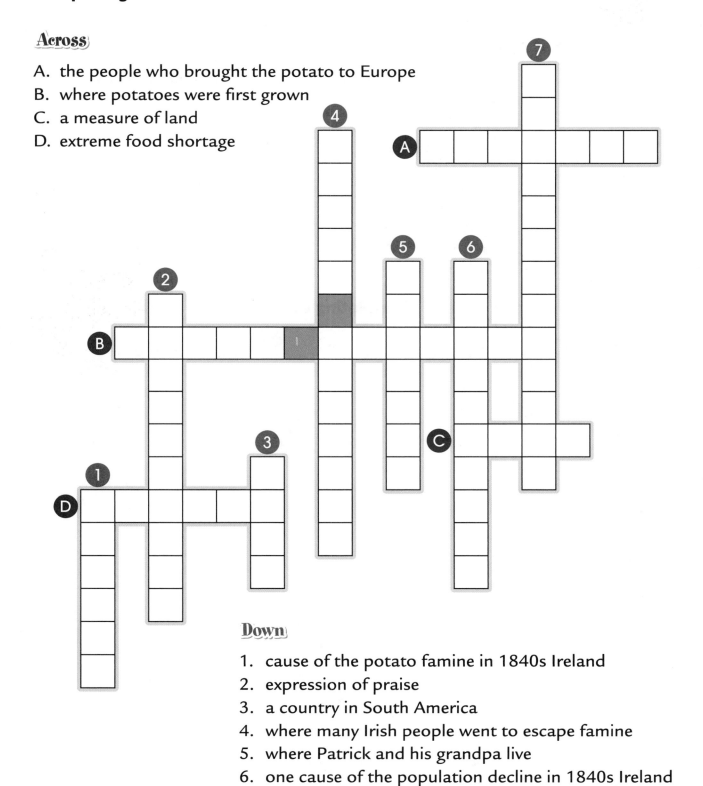

Down

1. cause of the potato famine in 1840s Ireland
2. expression of praise
3. a country in South America
4. where many Irish people went to escape famine
5. where Patrick and his grandpa live
6. one cause of the population decline in 1840s Ireland
7. Spanish conquerors of Mexico and Peru in the 1500s

Introduction to Participles

A **participle** is a word formed from a verb, such as "going" (present participle) and "gone" (past participle). We use the **present participle** for the progressive tenses. We use the **past participle** for the perfect tenses, as well as for the passive voice. Both present and past participles can be used as adjectives.

Examples: Erica is <u>writing</u> a story.
Erica was <u>writing</u> a story.
Erica will be <u>writing</u> a story.
Erica has <u>written</u> a story.
The story was <u>written</u> by Erica.
Erica used <u>writing</u> paper to write her story.
Erica produced a <u>written</u> piece of work!

B. Practise your participles by completing this chart.

Verb	Present Participle	Past Participle
1. dance		
2. give		
3. spread		
4. hear		
5. do		
6. speak		
7. rise		
8. choose		
9. draw		
10. see		
11. fly		

C. Write "present participle", "past participle", or "neither" for each underlined word.

1. The nutritious potato was first <u>grown</u> in South America. _____

2. The little boy <u>looked</u> at his grandfather. _____

3. People in Ireland were <u>starving</u> during the potato famine. _____

4. Farmers were <u>growing</u> potatoes in South America when the Spanish conquistadors entered Peru. _____

5. The Irish <u>took</u> their love of the potato with them to North America. _____

6. The potato is actually one of the most <u>loved</u> vegetables in the world! _____

D. Check the correct sentences. Put a cross and rewrite the wrong ones on the lines.

1. The chuckled grandfather described the goodness of potatoes.

2. The grandfather spoke about the beloved potato.

3. The Irish were seeking new land to grow potatoes when they moved to North America.

4. Many people the world over have choosing the potato as their favourite vegetable.

5. "The fungus has spreaded to my field as well," a sad farmer said.

_____

_____

_____

Asteroids

Much speculation has been made of the possibility of an asteroid colliding with Earth, and Hollywood has profited handsomely from movies depicting such a catastrophe. Today, scientists are studying the probability of such a collision and the chances of deflecting an asteroid heading toward Earth. Asteroid fragments that have struck Earth provide samples for scientists to examine. Many scientists attribute changes to Earth's geography and the extinction of dinosaurs to asteroids that crashed into Earth millions of years ago.

Asteroids are formed from material left over from the formation of the solar system approximately 4.5 billion years ago. Most asteroids orbit the sun between Mars and Jupiter. This region is called the asteroid belt and contains millions of asteroids of varying sizes. The largest is Ceres, which is 950 kilometres in diameter.

Asteroids were first spotted by telescope in 1801. In 1991, the NASA spacecraft Galileo was the first to observe an asteroid using the fly-by method. In 2001, NASA landed a spacecraft on the asteroid Eros and was able to do extensive scientific research.

Recent research tells us that there is little likelihood of a Near-Earth Object (NEO) striking Earth. In fact, statistics suggest that a NEO strikes Earth once or twice every million years. If one did strike, it would destroy a fraction of the Earth and kill a portion of the population.

Fortunately, unlike most natural disasters, an asteroid colliding with Earth may be avoidable. Scientists believe that an asteroid would pass near Earth many times before striking. This should give enough warning time to plan to deflect the asteroid from its path. The key to protecting ourselves, though, is not so much in the defence upon the threat of a collision, but in the finding

A. Write 1 to 5 to put the events in order.

☐ Scientists first spotted asteroids by telescope.

☐ The solar system was formed.

☐ A NASA spacecraft landed on asteroid Eros and did extensive research.

☐ The left-over material from the solar system formed the asteroid belt.

☐ The NASA spacecraft Galileo observed an asteroid using the fly-by method.

B. Read the following statements and decide whether they are true or false. Rewrite the false ones to make them true.

1. Hollywood has made great profits from movies depicting the extinction of dinosaurs.

    _____

2. Scientists are studying the possibility of destroying an asteroid heading toward Earth.

    _____

3. The asteroid belt lies between Mars and Jupiter.

    _____

4. The possibility of a Near-Earth Object colliding with Earth is great.

    _____

5. An asteroid would pass near Earth many times before striking Earth.

    _____

6. The key to protecting Earth is in the defence upon the threat of a collision.

    _____

The Present Perfect Tense

The **present perfect tense** is a kind of "combination" of the past and the present: used for recent actions that affect the present. It is also used for recent actions with no definite time (as indicated by words like "so far", "yet", "lately", "recently", "ever", "never", and "always"). We use the simple form for actions that started and ended in the past. We use the progressive form for actions that started in the past but are still going on.

Examples: Vincent <u>has got</u> into trouble and is grounded for a week.
<u>Have you had</u> lunch yet?
Chris <u>has been practising</u> the trumpet for a month now.

C.   Circle the correct answers.

1. _____ Sara ever thought about attending heritage classes?

   A. Did   B. Has   C. Will

2. Toby has _____ painting the walls and has started building shelves.

   A. been finishing   B. finished   C. finish

3. I have _____ my phone number to strangers.

   A. never gave   B. never given   C. gave

4. Scientists are studying the asteroid fragments that _____ Earth.

   A. have been striking   B. has struck   C. have struck

5. Have you _____ why the dinosaur became extinct?

   A. ever wonder   B. ever wondered   C. wondering

6. Sam _____ on a sculpture since January.

   A. has been working   B. worked   C. has worked

7. I _____ that you would come and am so glad that you are here!

   A. have been hoping   B. have hoped   C. hoped

D. **Underline the correct tenses in this paragraph.**

Ever since her father and sister saved her life that winter morning, Amy 1. has become / has been becoming such a doll around the house. She no longer 2. has thrown / throws her regular temper tantrums and she listens to what others have to say before giving her own opinion. She used to break things in her room, especially when she 3. did not get / has not got her way. But she has since 4. changed / been changing . She is now less selfish and more grateful. Everyone in the house is still in awe of Amy's "transformation", but her parents 5. are / have been certainly glad that they now have a less difficult, more cheerful daughter.

E. **Use these verbs to make sentences in the simple present perfect tense and the present perfect progressive tense.**

1. profit

   _____

   _____

2. study

   _____

   _____

3. protect

   _____

   _____

Seven or Eight Summits?

Everyone knows that the world's tallest mountain is Mount Everest. Mountain climbers all over the world dream of climbing it. But ever since Tenzing Norgay and Edmund Hillary first reached its summit in 1953, over 4000 people have done so themselves. Where do these people head for their next challenge?

Many climbers think about conquering "The Seven Summits" – that is, to climb the highest mountain on each of the seven continents. Take a look at the chart below:

Mountain	Height (metres)	Location
Everest	8848	Nepal and Tibet, Asia
Aconcagua	6962	Argentina, South America
McKinley	6195	Alaska, North America
Kilimanjaro	5963	Tanzania, Africa
Elbrus	5633	Russia, Europe
Vinson Massif	4897	Ellsworth Range, Antarctica
Kosciuszko	2228	New South Wales, Australia
Carstensz Pyramid	4884	Irian Jaya, Indonesia

You're right! There are *eight* mountain peaks listed here. Some people think that Australia is not a continent by itself, but should include the Indonesian *archipelago* ("group of islands") to its north. We call this area of land and water *Australasia*. So, if we consider Australasia instead of Australia as a continent, then Carstensz Pyramid is the seventh summit.

There is another reason why some people think that Mount Kosciuszko should not be on the list: it is too easy to climb! In fact, you can even ride a bicycle all the way to the top.

To date, about 100 people have climbed to the top of all eight summits. Pat Morrow, a Canadian mountaineer, author, explorer, and filmmaker, was the first person to have done it.

A. Write the correct words from the passage beside the following.

1. _____ : "group of islands"

2. _____ : Australia and the land and water to its north

3. _____ : the world's tallest mountain

4. _____ : the continent of the third summit

5. _____ : the summit in South America

6. _____ : the continent with the highest summit

7. _____ : the summit that is the easiest to reach

8. _____ : the first to have climbed all eight summits

B. Give your opinions.

1. Many adventurers think about "conquering" Mount Everest, but many people in Tibet, for example, prefer to walk around it. Are mountains to be conquered, or are they to be admired?

_____

_____

_____

_____

2. Over 4000 people have reached the summit of Mount Everest since 1953, and about 100 people have climbed to the top of all eight summits. Does this say anything about human nature? If so, what does it say? If not, explain.

_____

_____

_____

_____

Frequently Confused Words

We often confuse words that have similar sound or spelling, so it is always useful to check with a dictionary to make sure we are using the right word.

Example: <u>Its</u> Friday today. (✗)
<u>It's</u> Friday today. (✔)

C.   Fill in the blanks with the correct words.

Gregory is a spirited boy who is always full of (presence, presents) 1._____ . Now that he is a little older, he has an even better sense of humour (than, then) 2._____ before. And he has grown so much taller! His grandparents could not believe (they're, their) 3._____ eyes when they visited him this summer. "We (could of, could've) 4._____ picked out some longer pants for you," his grandma said. The ones we bought you (wood, would) 5._____ probably not fit you." Pointing at his bookshelf, Gregory replied, "You forgot that I was (already, all ready) 6._____ as tall as that bookshelf back in Christmas, Grandma? But that's okay! I'm going to try on these pants. They look pretty (lose, loose) 7._____ !"

D.   Underline the wrong word in each sentence and write the correct one.

1.   Whose the one that spelled "Kilimanjaro" correctly?   _____

2.   "Were going to walk around the mountain," says Bill. "Want to come?"   _____

3.   The school principle came to chat with our teacher.   _____

E. **Write sentences to show how the words in each pair have different meanings.**

1. beside/besides

_____

_____

2. you're/your

_____

_____

3. advice/advise

_____

_____

4. thorough/through

_____

_____

F. **Read what Kelly says and make up more sentences.**

Can you think of more frequently confused words? Write them down and make up your own sentences to show how their meanings are different.

1. _____

_____

_____

2. _____

_____

_____

The Aral Sea in Central Asia is disappearing. It used to be the world's fourth largest lake. It had an area of 66 000 square kilometres and a volume of more than 1000 cubic kilometres. Fishermen used to have catches of 40 000 tonnes a year. The river deltas, marshes, and wetlands around it covered 550 000 hectares, and were once home to many fish, animal, and bird species.

But in the 1960s, planners in the former Soviet Union decided to make Central Asia the main supplier of raw cotton. This was not a smart decision. The land was dry, so irrigation was necessary. To these government planners, the Aral Sea seemed like a good place to get the water. The amount of irrigated land in Central Asia grew from 4.5 million hectares in 1960 to 7 million hectares 20 years later. The amount of water taken from the Aral Sea doubled. At the same time, many people moved into the area, and the population rose from 14 million to about 27 million.

The irrigated land became salty from using this water. Pesticides and fertilizers were used on the cotton fields, polluting the surface water and groundwater. The delta marshes and wetlands began to disappear. By 1990, more than 95 per cent of the marshes and wetlands had become sandy deserts. The surface of the Aral Sea reduced in size by half, and its volume reduced by three-quarters.

The Disappearing Aral Sea

Most of the fish in the Aral Sea and the wildlife around it are now gone. In 1982, commercial fishing operations ceased. Towns and villages that used to be on the seashore are now 70 km away from it. People in these communities have become sick. In the past 20 years, there has been a great increase in bronchitis as well as kidney and liver diseases. Cancer and arthritic diseases have increased by more than 60 times! The infant mortality rate in this area is near the highest in the world.

Five Central Asian states, who became independent countries after the former Soviet Union came apart in the 1990s, are working to solve the problems of the disappearing Aral Sea through the International Fund for Saving the Aral Sea (IFAS). Only time will tell if it is already too late.

A.   Answer these questions.

1.   Why was water taken from the Aral Sea in the 1960s?

_____

_____

_____

2.   How has the government planners' decision affected vegetation and wildlife?

_____

_____

_____

3.   How have the people in the area been affected?

_____

_____

_____

4.   In the future, what do you suggest government planners should do before making economic decisions?

_____

_____

_____

5.   How do you think you can help the communities around the Aral Sea?

_____

_____

_____

Punctuation to Pause or Complete a Sentence

To complete a sentence, we use:
· a **period**.
· a **question mark**.
· an **exclamation mark**.

We use **quotation marks**:
· for sentences in direct speech.
· for borrowed sentences (e.g. from a book or a person).
· for words being specially talked about (e.g. given as a definition).

We use a **comma**:
· to show a pause in a sentence.
· instead of a period to end a sentence in certain instances of direct speech.

B. Check the sentences with correct punctuation. Put a cross and rewrite the wrong ones with correct punctuation.

1. IFAS stands for "International Fund for Saving the Aral Sea".

2. Gone, are the wildlife around the Aral Sea.

3. It is a warning sign that, the infant mortality rate is at a record high.

4. "Too many diseases are on the rise!" My grandmother exclaims.

5. They wanted to plant cotton, but they had to irrigate the land first.

6. "I'll give you a concrete plan once I have it ready." says Gail.

7. "Do you think there's still time to save the Aral Sea?" Wanda asks.

8. To some people, the president of the U.S. is referred to as Dubya.

The Apostrophe

We use an **apostrophe** to:
· indicate possession.
· indicate the location of missing letters in a contraction.
· make special plural forms.

Examples: This is Erica's desk.
             I've written my name here.
             There are a lot of o's in "Scooby Doo"!

C.   Help Michelle write the missing apostrophes in her speech.

Hello everybody. Im Marmalade. My real name is actually Michelle, but everyone calls me "Marmalade" because I love jam. The nickname somehow stuck. Im a very messy kid. My mom has told me many, many times to clean up the mess in my room, but Im always too busy with homework, or too lazy to ever get around to it. Theres a sign on my door that says "Marmalades Room", which I made in my Senior Kindergarten class. Because my room has been in a state of mess for the past six years, my mom teases me all the time. She would ask, "Why dont you make a new sign? `Marmalades Mess` would be a pretty cute one, wouldnt it?"

To that Id answer, "There are too many ms in `Marmalades Mess`. In any case, my room will never be tidy, so I have all the time in the world to make a new sign. Maybe Ill make one that says "Chaos Within. Watch Your Step." Ill paint the words neon green on black bristol board. Wouldnt that be sharp?

All about *Salt*

Salt. We use it every day. But how much do you really know about the stuff you sprinkle on your food? It's a very important resource.

Civilizations grew and declined around the availability of salt. Control over salt supplies meant power over life and death. In pre-industrial times, salt was a scarce item, available only as salt cakes from seashores and salt lakes, or from what was visible in the rocky outcrops of arid regions.

Salt routes were created, joining Europe, Africa, and the Middle East. Venice's wealth was based on salt. In Egypt, salt was valued as a preservative and an antiseptic. The Egyptians used a form of salt in their mummification process. In the Roman era, salt was used to pay for slaves, and also to pay the soldiers of the Roman Empire.

Salt is essential for good health. We would die without it. Our body contains as much as 250 grams of salts – electrolytes in the form of chloride, calcium, magnesium, potassium – and sodium. These mineral salts are needed for muscle coordination, nerve and heart function, and concentration. Salt is a good skin softener, too. The Egyptians were the first to use salt in the bath. They combined alkaline salts with animal and vegetable oils to create the first kind of soap.

You can cook with it, light your fire with it, and clean pots and pans with it. It is the only non-biological food we routinely eat (water is the only non-biological fluid that we routinely drink). We enjoy salt as a food preservative and a flavour enhancer. It is one of only four tastes the human tongue can distinguish (sour, sweet, and bitter being the others).

With industrialization, salt is now plentiful, and mined all over the world. There are many kinds of commercial salts available to us today: sea salt, kosher salt, rock salt, table salt (iodized or plain), canning and pickling salt, popcorn salt (extra-fine grains make it stick better to the popcorn), lite (low sodium) salt, and even salt substitutes.

Who would have guessed that so much could be said about a tiny grain of salt?

A.   Write the root words of these words from the passage.

1.   civilizations _____

2.   availability _____

3.   preservative _____

4.   mummification _____

5.   softener _____

6.   industrialization _____

7.   commercial _____

8.   coordination _____

9.   plentiful _____

10.   biological _____

B.   Read the following statements and decide whether they are true or false. Rewrite the false ones to make them true.

1.   In the old days, most of the salt was found in Venice.

_____

2.   Salt was an important resource in the old days.

_____

3.   Our bodies need salt to produce calcium and sodium.

_____

4.   Salt enhances flavour and allows us to distinguish the four tastes.

_____

5.   The Romans were the first to make soap with salt.

_____

6.   Slaves were paid salt for their services.

_____

7.   Nowadays, there is an abundance of salt all over the world.

_____

Colons and Semicolons

We use a **colon**:
· to introduce a list of items or a quotation.
· to set off a concluding statement.
· between two clauses when the second explains the first.

We use a **semicolon**:
· in place of a conjunction to join two closely related clauses or sentences.
· between a series of items when the items are long or contain commas within.

C. Add colons or semicolons where needed in the following sentences.

1. It was freezing this morning the temperature dropped to -10°C.

2. Our coach told us to take these items with us a bat, a helmet, and a glove.

3. The package finally arrived it was the latest video game console.

4. Here is a list of exercises she does in every session weightlifting, which builds her upper body strength running, which builds up her endurance biking, which strengthens her leg muscles.

5. Remember this when one door closes, another opens.

6. The new company is recruiting the following personnel a secretary, two sales representatives, and a marketing executive.

7. We tried to stage a comeback however we couldn't make it in the end.

8. We all overlooked one point no one actually had all the information.

9. At the party, Joanne met the following people Miranda, her one-time best friend Rob, the son of Mrs. Weir, her history teacher Patricia, her next-door neighbour when she stayed in Peterborough, and Justin, the class clown.

Parentheses

We use **parentheses** to:
- enclose additional information.
- add a comment to a statement.
- show letters and numbers that designate a series of items.

D. Place parentheses where needed in the following sentences.

1. The flight AC068 took 11 hours non-stop to reach the city.

2. The camp warden told the children to 1 switch off all the lights at ten, 2 get up at seven, and 3 do morning exercise at half past seven.

3. The seminar details to be confirmed will include Dr. John Walsh as one of the speakers.

4. Samuel Watt the boy we used to tease is now a successful business executive.

5. Members should a apply in person, b pay a one-time fee of $50, and c attend a half-day training course.

6. Please refer to the map inset for the exact route to Bowmanville.

7. The collection believed to be donated by the Rodman family is now on display in the local museum.

8. The starting pitcher ERA 3.75 has not lost a game since July 4.

9. As he is the one handling the complaint ref. C20-786-03 dated March 23, 2014, you should seek clarification from him.

10. The graph see attached indicates an upward trend between 2011 and 2014.

Pauline Johnson

Pauline Johnson was born on March 10, 1861, near Brantford, Ontario, the daughter of the Mohawk Chief, G.H. Johnson, and an Englishwoman named Emily Howells. She became a much-loved poet in the late 19th and early 20th centuries, writing of both her Aboriginal and European roots.

The Corn Husker

Hard by the Indian lodges, where the bush
Breaks in a clearing, through ill-fashioned fields,
She comes to labour, when the first still hush
Of autumn follows large and recent yields.

Age in her fingers, hunger in her face,
Her shoulders stooped with weight of work and years,
But rich in tawny colouring of her race,
She comes a-field to strip the purple ears.

And all her thoughts are with the days gone by,
Ere might's injustice banished from their lands
Her people, that today unheeded lie,
Like the dead husks that rustle through her hands.

Canada (an acrostic poem)

Crown of her, young Vancouver; crest of her, old Quebec;
Atlantic and far Pacific sweeping her, keel to deck.
North of her, ice and arctics; southward a rival's stealth;
Aloft, her Empire's pennant; below, her nation's wealth.
Daughter of men and markets, bearing within her hold,
Appraised at highest value, cargoes of grain and gold.

A. Match the words with the meanings. Write the correct letters.

1. hush _____   **A** clear area in a forest

2. yields _____   **B** an older form of "before"

3. clearing _____   **C** make sounds like leaves blown in the wind

4. unheeded _____   **D** crops that are produced

5. might _____   **E** stillness or silence

6. ere _____   **F** heads of corn

7. rustle _____   **G** disregarded

8. ears _____   **H** power

B. Quote lines from Pauline Johnson's poems for the following.

1. In "The Corn Husker":

a. Which lines tell you about the corn husker's physical appearance?

_____

_____

_____

b. Which lines tell you that the corn husker's people had been forced out of their land, and that they are now dead?

_____

_____

2. In "Canada (an acrostic poem)":

a. Which line tells of Canada's natural resources?

_____

b. Which line reflects Canada's motto, "From sea to sea"?

_____

Phrases

There are three types of **phrases: noun phrases, adjective phrases,** and **adverb phrases.** A noun phrase contains a noun and other words like adjectives. An adjective phrase describes a noun. An adverb phrase describes a verb.

Examples: The woman comes to harvest <u>the purple ears</u>. (noun phrase)
She is in a field <u>of her dreams</u>. (adjective phrase)
She harvests <u>in the season of falling leaves</u>. (adverb phrase)

C.   Write "noun", "adjective", or "adverb" for each underlined phrase.

1. The bush breaks <u>in a clearing</u>. _____

2. The works <u>about the poet's roots</u> are very personal. _____

3. She begins work when the still hush of autumn follows <u>large and recent yields</u>. _____

4. The woman is rich in <u>the tawny colouring</u> of her race. _____

5. The dead leaves rustle <u>through her hands</u>. _____

6. Cargoes <u>of grain and gold</u> are appraised at the highest value. _____

7. The woman <u>from the cornfield</u> returns with the season's harvest. _____

8. They all gather <u>around a glowing campfire</u>. _____

9. Pauline Johnson was the daughter of an Englishwoman <u>named Emily Howells</u>. _____

10. The woman is walking <u>by the Indian lodges</u>. _____

11. The one <u>leaving us now</u> will soon return. _____

12. Where have <u>the little children</u> gone? _____

D. **Complete each sentence using a noun phrase, an adjective phrase, or an adverb phrase.**

1. _____

   are all lined up in front of the school bus. (noun phrase)

2. The children and their teachers have arrived at the lodge and will

   soon be skiing _____ . (adverb phrase)

3. The hill _____ has the steepest slope of all. (adjective phrase)

4. Whenever it is someone's birthday in class, we get to have

   _____ . (noun phrase)

5. It is so strange that these dreams have been repeating themselves

   _____ . (adverb phrase)

6. The flowers _____ are blowing lazily in the late afternoon breeze. (adjective phrase)

E. **Think about an interesting day of your week so far. Write a journal entry about it containing the three types of phrases.**

_____

_____

_____

_____

_____

_____

_____

_____

Temperatures around the world are getting warmer. Scientists say that the Earth is heating up. There is evidence to support this. Polar ice shelves are breaking into small pieces. Glaciers all over the world are melting. Polar bears are drowning because the ice floes they walk on are melting away. Areas of dry land are expanding, and drought occurs more often now. Tropical diseases are spreading into semi-tropical areas. Some people also say that strange weather patterns are caused by global warming.

Some say that what is happening now is part of a natural cycle, but a more popular belief is that the Earth is heating up because human activity is increasing the greenhouse effect. The greenhouse effect occurs naturally. Our Earth has a layer of atmosphere around it. The sun's rays pass through this layer. Some of this radiation bounces off the Earth back into outer space but most stays around the Earth. This makes the Earth about 16 degrees Celsius warmer than it would otherwise be. But human activities are putting greenhouse gases into the atmosphere, blocking most of the radiation from leaving. So the Earth is getting warmer.

Global Climate Change
Facing the Future

There is much we can do to slow down global warming. First, we must demand that our governments make better choices. We must make our governments lessen our need for fossil fuels such as coal and oil (they create greenhouse gases) by developing alternative sources of energy such as solar, tidal, hydroelectric, and geothermal power. We must tell our governments to provide more mass transit options, make more parks, create more recycling programs, and plant more trees.

We can also do these things with our own families. We can share car rides, take public transportation, and ride our bikes more. We can plant trees and recycle things, too. We can turn off the lights and our computers when we don't need them. We can try to live a "greener" life. It's not too late, but we must act now!

A. Choose and underline the main idea of each paragraph.

Paragraph One

A. Scientists find evidence of the Earth getting warmer.

B. Strange weather patterns are caused by global warming.

C. Polar bears drown as a result of melting ice floes.

Paragraph Two

A. The Earth is surrounded by the atmosphere but the sun's rays can pass through it.

B. The greenhouse effect is a natural occurence but human activities increase greenhouse gases, making the Earth warmer.

C. People believe that the greenhouse effect is a natural occurence.

Paragraph Three

A. We can help slow down global warming.

B. Governments should plant more trees to slow down global warming.

C. We must demand that our governments make better choices.

Paragraph Four

A. We can ride our bikes more.

B. We must act now to stop global warming.

C. We can live a greener life to slow down global warming.

B. Read the following statements. Put a cross for the ones that are not causes of global warming.

1. Scientists are looking into a wider use of solar energy.   _____

2. More and more people are commuting on bikes.   _____

3. Coal is burned to generate electricity.   _____

4. The traffic is clogged due to more and more cars on roads.   _____

5. Glaciers all over the world show signs of gradual melting.   _____

Clauses

Clauses can be independent or dependent. An **independent clause** has a complete meaning and can stand on its own as a sentence.

A **dependent clause** relies on an independent clause to make its meaning complete. It cannot stand on its own.

Example: Although they suffered a loss, the team remained confident.
                     (dependent clause)   (independent clause)

C.   State whether the underlined clause is an independent clause (IND) or a dependent clause (D).

1.   <u>As soon as I stepped into the room</u>, the bridegroom came to greet me.   _____

2.   <u>If we drop this game</u>, we won't have a chance for the play-offs.   _____

3.   Whenever he is free, <u>he plays video games in his room</u>.   _____

4.   They did not show up <u>because they were given the wrong address</u>.   _____

5.   <u>Heather was excited</u> when she realized that hers was the winning ticket.   _____

6.   <u>We will go</u> whether or not the weather is fine.   _____

D.   Join each of the following pairs of sentences by changing one sentence into a dependent clause. Make any other necessary changes.

1.   The umpire decided to cancel the game. It was raining heavily.

_____

_____

2.   He knew his chance of winning was slim. He entered the race.

_____

_____

3. I was walking down the street. I ran into Priscilla's cousin.

_____

_____

4. We are best friends. I have no reason not to help you out again.

_____

_____

5. Cynthia was on the phone. Her parents returned home.

_____

_____

6. They seldom contact each other. Ronald and Tony are twin brothers.

_____

_____

E. Add a dependent or an independent clause to each of the following sentences.

1. Everyone was screaming _____

_____ .

2. I will let you know _____ .

3. Sandra takes her puppy with her _____

_____ .

4. If they don't come back by ten, _____

_____ .

5. Since we are ahead of schedule, _____

_____ .

My Grandma died last night. She had cancer. Mom told me a year ago that Grandma was sick, but that there was treatment available and we were going to give it a try. Grandma had to go through something called chemotherapy. She showed me her calendar, in which she had drawn a star on each date of her "chemo" appointments. On those days, a family member or a friend would take her to the hospital. Before the appointment, they would do something fun together, like visit an art gallery or get a pedicure.

One day it was my turn to take Grandma to her chemotherapy. We took the bus to a park. There was a sculpture garden and we enjoyed looking at all the statues. We told each other which statues were our favourites.

But when Grandma came home after these chemo sessions, she did not feel very well. Soon, her hair started to fall out, so Mom bought us all matching scarves to wear on our heads. Dad took our photo.

Grandma's cancer was strong. Sometimes she looked and felt good, but she was still sick, so she moved in with us. We started a project together. When she moved in, she brought boxes of photos and other papers with her. Mom bought a lot of albums. Then Mom moved our computer next to Grandma's bed. Grandma put the photos into the albums, starting from when she was young. She would tell me stories about the photos, and I would type them on the computer and print out the pages. Sometimes Grandma would even give me and my brother pieces of advice, and made sure that I typed those in too, exactly the way she said them.

"Make sure you learn how to be organized, Tina," she would say. "Even kids should have their own filing cabinet." Or, she would say, "Think for yourself, Tina. Don't let anyone make you do what you know in your heart is a bad idea."

Tina and Grandma's Project

Grandma and I did not have the chance to finish the project, however. There are a dozen more photos to go, so Mom is going to help me with them. I really miss Grandma, but I am glad that my brother and I have these books. I am glad that I learned the story of my Grandma's life. And I will keep her advice in mind.

A. Write your own responses.

1. Why did Grandma's family and friends take her out to do something fun before every chemotherapy session?

   _____

   _____

   _____

2. When Grandma's hair began falling out, why did Tina's mother buy everyone the same scarves to wear on their heads?

   _____

   _____

   _____

3. For Tina, what was the significance of doing her project with Grandma? If you were in Tina's shoes, what would your project with your grandma be?

   _____

   _____

   _____

   _____

   _____

4. It is important to listen to the elderly because they are full of wisdom. When was the last time you took advice from someone older than you? How did you benefit from the advice?

   _____

   _____

   _____

   _____

Conjunctions

Conjunctions are words that connect clauses together into sentences. **Coordinating conjunctions** (e.g. "and", "or") connect independent clauses. **Subordinating conjunctions** (e.g. "because", "so", and "while") connect dependent clauses to independent clauses. Some conjunctions are made up of two or more words.

Examples: Lisa is on time <u>but</u> her friend is late.

Her friend is late <u>because</u> the train was delayed.

Lisa stayed longer <u>so that</u> she would see her friend.

B.   Write "coordinating" or "subordinating" for the conjunction in each sentence.

1. I will not leave the party unless my friend wants to go home.   _____

2. Jessie wants to finish her homework fast but the TV is distracting her.   _____

3. Maria is practising a difficult song because she wants to impress her parents.   _____

4. The tree glitters and the music continues.   _____

5. Alana's house is nearby so we will go there.   _____

6. This is the assignment that Mrs. McKell was very happy with.   _____

7. By the time you arrive, everything will be in place.   _____

8. We could have a meal or we could just go for ice cream.   _____

9. If you stay that way, I will not play with you.   _____

10. I will turn off the TV as soon as I hear Mom's car pulling up on the driveway.   _____

C. **Connect the clauses that go together. Write the numbers. Then write the complete sentences with the correct conjunctions and punctuation.**

1 Maria will perform her tune

2 we need to buy some cookie cutters

3 Mom is going to stuff the turkey

4 Christopher did not make it to the last round of the contest

5 you have such a good sense of colour

_____ we start preparing the dough

_____ he remained in good spirit

_____ she feels she can sing it in her sleep

_____ she has finished chopping the onions

_____ you can help me pick out a dress that looks good on me

since   before   after   when   even though

1. _____

_____

2. _____

_____

3. _____

_____

4. _____

_____

5. _____

_____

WRITING

Humankind's Greatest Invention

Writing is fun, but it can also be a serious endeavour. Writing can be art or science. Writing is a great way to communicate information and feelings. Writing can inform and entertain. It can incite. It can reassure. It can change people's lives. It can change the world. And it is something we can all do. Writing is humankind's greatest invention.

Evidence of man's earliest attempt to communicate by "writing" things down can be found in caves. Yes, even cavemen wanted to make note of their activities; their 30 000-year-old hunting journals have been found on the walls in caves near Avignon, France.

Egyptian civilization also had its own form of picture art/communication, called hieroglyphs. The ancient Assyrians (in what is now northern Iraq) had a system called cuneiform. The Chinese pictographic system of writing began as early as the 15th century BCE. Over time, all of these pictographic systems incorporated phonetic elements as well. The Korean and Japanese "alphabets", developed later, are phonetic in nature, although today, Japan also incorporates the Chinese writing system into its language. Other Asian languages, such as Thai, are also phonetic in nature, meaning that the written symbols are based on sounds, not pictures or ideas.

The western alphabet was first developed in the Middle East, by the Phoenicians, in the area that is now Lebanon (hence, the term "phonetic"). With this phonetic system, we need only a small number of symbols, which can be combined in an unlimited number of ways, to write all the words we need. It is generally agreed that pictograph-based languages, such as Chinese, are harder to master, but not impossible. For example, while there are 130 000 Chinese characters in existence, the average Chinese person needs to know only about 2000 to be able to read the newspaper.

From cave-wall art to the printing press and the World Wide Web, the expression of ideas through writing – and the dissemination of these ideas – has become accessible to so many people. Through blogs, for example, we can know what people are thinking and feeling about things on the other side of the world! We are truly living in a global village.

A. **Write about the following terms that appear in the passage.**

Example: cave-wall art: <u>the earliest form of "writing"</u>

1. hieroglyphs: _____

2. the Thai language: _____

3. cuneiform: _____

4. phonetic-based language: _____

5. pictograph-based language: _____

6. the Chinese writing system: _____

7. Phoenicians: _____

B. **Answer these questions.**

1. What was the earliest attempt of human beings to communicate by "writing"?

_____

_____

2. Where did the western alphabet originate?

_____

_____

3. Explain briefly the characteristics of the Japanese language.

_____

_____

4. Which are easier to learn, phonetic-based or pictograph-based languages?

_____

5. What, according to the writer, is the most important use of writing?

_____

Compound and Complex Sentences

A **compound sentence** is made up of two or more independent clauses joined together by conjunctions.

A **complex sentence** is made up of an independent clause with one or more dependent clauses.

Examples: They remained silent and they refused to budge. (compound)
However hard the interrogator tried, they remained silent. (complex)

C.   State whether the following sentences are compound (CP) or complex (CX).

1.   You may be able to meet with Joanne at the party but there is no guarantee.   _____

2.   We can celebrate in his home or we can have a party at a restaurant.   _____

3.   Despite many attempts, he could not open the program.   _____

4.   Even if you don't support me, I'll go ahead with my plan.   _____

5.   The goalie made a wrong move and the puck slipped past him into the net.   _____

6.   They rushed to the hospital as soon as they heard the news.   _____

D.   Add an independent clause to each of the following sentences to make it a compound sentence.

1.   I was totally disappointed.

_____

_____

2.   This seems to be the only solution.

_____

_____

3. The show was about to start.

_____

_____

4. The dog sniffed around.

_____

_____

5. The game was delayed.

_____

_____

_____

_____

E. Change the following compound sentences to complex sentences. Make any other necessary changes.

1. We did not go to the show but we went skating instead.

_____

_____

2. He tried very hard but he did not make it in the end.

_____

_____

3. The questions were very tricky and no one could get all of them right.

_____

_____

4. The water was freezing but the swimmers dived in all the same.

_____

_____

Bear Attack

More and more people like backpacking and hiking. Is there anything that one cannot appreciate about the rugged mountainous terrain, fresh air, and the majestic beauty of the wilderness? Yet a lot of us forget that many of the original inhabitants of these areas still live there, including bears.

Bears are more curious than aggressive. They may approach you, but will usually run away if they sense that you are aware of their presence. It is not unusual to see bears on the trail during daylight hours although most bear sightings are in the evening.

On the rare occasion you run into a bear, there are ways to protect yourself. Back away slowly and cautiously. Watch the bear's reaction, but do not make eye contact with the bear as it may see it as a threat. If the bear follows you, stop and hold your ground. Keep a cool head. The worst thing you can do is panic. Do not turn and run as this may trigger the bear's predatory instinct to chase you, and you will never outrun a bear because it moves much faster than you think. The average bear can run up to 40 kilometres per hour! Never try to climb a tree either as bears are better climbers than you!

Also, do not remove your backpack. Some people think that the extra weight will hamper their agility in a confrontation with a bear. But in fact, your backpack provides extra protection for your body if the bear grabs or rolls you.

If the bear looks like it is going to attack, drop to the ground. Cover your head, chest, and abdomen by curling yourself up into a tight ball. These are the crucial areas to be protected. Do not struggle or scream. Usually, if you allow the bear to roll you while you are still in a tight ball, the bear will deem you dead and think the threat has been removed. It will give up and wander away.

A. Write the dos and don'ts when confronting a bear.

When Confronting a **Bear**

Dos and Don'ts

Dos

- _____
- _____
- _____
- _____
- _____
- _____

Don'ts

- _____
- _____
- _____
- _____
- _____
- _____

Compound-Complex Sentences

When a sentence is made up of two or more independent clauses joined together by conjunctions, with one or more dependent clauses, it is called a **compound-complex sentence**.

Example: As soon as I entered the room, the host greeted me and he led me to his mother.

B.   Check the compound-complex sentences.

1. Most bears are shy of people and they rarely attack unless provoked. ☐

2. When you go camping, make sure you store food in bear-proof containers and place them far away from your camp. ☐

3. After the show, Ella and her brother met their friends at a cozy French restaurant. ☐

4. The game continued although rain was pouring down and the players were all drenched to the skin. ☐

5. Whenever my parents are away, I stay at my grandparents' place or Grandma comes over to look after me. ☐

6. They waited until morning came and the storm was over before they headed out to sea again. ☐

7. My brother and I want to get a gift for Mom but we have no idea what to buy, so we've decided to ask Dad for some suggestions. ☐

8. Someone broke into our neighbour's house and stole all their precious belongings when they were out of town last weekend. ☐

9. When the accident happened, Kate tried to help even though she was scared. ☐

C. **Expand each of the following sentences or dependent clauses to make a compound-complex sentence.**

Compound-
Complex
Sentence

1. The grizzly bear stood up.

   _____

   _____

2. The dogs suddenly stopped growling.

   _____

   _____

3. He stared at me.

   _____

   _____

4. The guide pointed to the summit.

   _____

   _____

5. Although we haven't had the faintest clue, _____

   _____ .

6. Because we missed the last train, _____

   _____ .

7. When they heard the news, _____

   _____ .

8. Since they all came from the same team, _____

   _____ .

Every year since 1971, Nova Scotia has given an evergreen tree as a special Christmas gift to the people of Boston. The tree arrives in November, and stands in Boston Common, the city's prime location, through the winter season. How and why did this tradition of friendship start?

In the afternoon of December 6, 1917, the Massachusetts Committee on Public Safety received a telegram from Halifax, telling them that half the city of Halifax was in ruins, and that there were thousands of casualties. A ship filled with munitions had exploded in Halifax Harbour. Immediately, the governor of Massachusetts, Samuel McCall, formed the Halifax Relief Expedition. By nightfall, a relief train supplied with doctors and desperately needed materials was heading north to Nova Scotia. More followed: doctors from Harvard Medical School and the Massachusetts State Guard Medical Unit set up two emergency hospitals. Non-governmental organizations, such as the Christian Scientists, sent another trainload of clothing, food, money, and medical officers.

A Tree for Boston

Back in Boston, a concert featuring the Boston Symphony, opera singer Nellie Melba, and violinist Fritz Kreisler, performed to a sellout crowd and raised thousands of dollars for the Halifax relief effort. A convoy of trucks laden with needed items was dispatched by the Massachusetts Automobile Club. The people of Boston rushed to Boston Harbour to fill a relief boat with supplies.

A year later, one of Nova Scotia's finest evergreens was delivered to Boston, and since 1971, the gesture has become an annual tradition. Chosen by an official from the Nova Scotia Department of Natural Resources, the tree must meet the following specifications: approximately 15 metres high, medium to heavy density of branches, healthy with good colour, and a uniform shape. The tree is a "thank you" from Nova Scotians to Bostonians for their assistance following the 1917 Halifax explosion.

A. Explain in no more than 80 words why Halifax gives an evergreen tree to Boston every year as a Christmas gift.

_____

_____

_____

_____

_____

_____

_____

_____

B. List how Bostonians helped Nova Scotians following the disastrous explosion in Halifax Harbour.

1. _____

    _____

2. _____

    _____

3. _____

    _____

4. _____

    _____

5. _____

    _____

6. _____

    _____

Adding Details with Descriptive Words

Descriptive words help us add details to what we write, making it more informative and interesting to read.

Example: The tree is a gift given by Nova Scotians to Bostonians.
The <u>evergreen</u> tree is a <u>special</u> <u>Christmas</u> gift <u>gratefully</u> given by Nova Scotians to Bostonians.

C.   Underline the descriptive words in the following sentences.

1.   The special gift from Nova Scotia stands tall and proud in the city's prime location – Boston Common.

2.   Immediately, the governor of Massachusetts formed the Halifax Relief Expedition.

3.   The people of Boston rushed to Boston Harbour to fill a relief boat with much-needed supplies.

4.   A year later, one of Nova Scotia's finest evergreens was delivered to Boston.

5.   Many consider Bostonians' assistance to be the first-ever disaster-relief story of the modern era.

D.   Add descriptive words to the following sentences.

1.   We watched a game between the Boston Red Sox and the Blue Jays last weekend.

_____

_____

2.   The Jays managed to come back at the bottom of the ninth inning.

_____

_____

3. The Sox fans were disappointed as their team had led by two runs until the bottom of the ninth.

    _____

    _____

4. The performance by the Sox's closer led to the upset.

    _____

    _____

E. Read the following paragraph and add descriptive words where appropriate. Make any necessary changes to the sentences.

The Frog Pond in the city of Boston is the coolest gathering place in Boston in winter, as you can join residents and visitors alike as they glide over the refrigerated surface. In 1997, people were able to skate on this type of surface for the first time in downtown Boston. The Frog Pond Skating Rink is now open from November to mid-March with at least 100 days of seasonal skating. After you take a spin on the ice, you can enjoy lunch or dinner nearby. Just beyond the Frog Pond, you will find many restaurants. From the restaurants to the shops in downtown Boston, there is so much to do and see that it can be dizzying, just like the feeling you get after your first spin on skates.

Charlotte Whitehead Ross

The First Female Physician of Quebec and Manitoba

Charlotte Whitehead was born in England in 1843. At the age of five, she moved to Montreal when her father, a railway engineer, got a job constructing the railroad there. Charlotte discovered she had an interest in medicine while nursing her chronically ill elder sister throughout the years. At 18, she married and started a family. Several years later, Charlotte said she wanted to be a doctor. Her husband supported her decision.

Unfortunately, Canadian medical schools did not accept women students at the time. Leaving behind her husband and three children, Charlotte sacrificed her family life in order to study medicine at the Women's Medical College in Philadelphia, United States. It took Charlotte five years to earn her medical degree. During that period, she gave birth to another child.

Upon completion of her degree, Charlotte returned to Montreal and set up a successful practice. Three years later in 1878, she moved to Manitoba, where her father and husband were building part of the Canadian Pacific Railway. In Manitoba, Charlotte was once again a busy doctor. Many of her patients were from the nearby lumber camps and railway camps. Charlotte found herself setting broken bones and amputating mangled limbs, in addition to delivering all of the babies in the area.

But Charlotte had been practising without a licence. She had applied for a doctor's licence in both Montreal and Winnipeg, but was refused. The Manitoba College of Physicians and Surgeons, an all-male board, wanted her to complete her studies at a Canadian medical college! Charlotte refused to leave her family or her patients to spend time studying what she already knew. So in 1887, she appealed to the Manitoba Legislature to grant her a licence but they, too, refused. Charlotte continued to practise without a licence until 1912. She died four years later in Winnipeg, at the age of 73.

In November of 1993, Charlotte was posthumously granted a medical licence. The Manitoba Legislature passed this resolution, brought forward by Member of the Legislative Assembly Sharon Carstairs, who wanted to pay tribute to "this courageous and dedicated pioneer and other women like her, who have never been properly honoured for the part they played in building this country."

A. **Read the following statements and decide whether they are true or false. Rewrite the false ones to make them true.**

1. Charlotte became interested in medicine while caring for her sister.

   _____

2. Canadian medical schools began to accept women students at the time that Charlotte decided to become a doctor.

   _____

   _____

3. Charlotte was a specialist who delivered babies.

   _____

4. The Manitoba Legislature granted Charlotte a licence in 1887.

   _____

5. Charlotte was never granted a medical licence during her life.

   _____

6. According to Sharon Carstairs, Charlotte helped build Canada.

   _____

B. **Imagine you are Charlotte. Write a journal entry about your busy day.**

   _____

   _____

   _____

   _____

   _____

   _____

   _____

   _____

Narrative Writing

We use **narrative writing** to tell a story. This type of writing often involves telling about events in **chronological order**. It may be told in either the first person ("I", "we") or the third person ("he", "she", "it", "they").

C. **Read the order of narration. Then use the given sentences to write a narrative paragraph about the first black Governor General of Canada.**

Order of Narration:

1. Tell when Michaelle Jean came to Canada.
2. Tell about her school years.
3. Tell about what she did in her career.
4. Tell when she was appointed Governor General.

- By 2004, she began her own show, *Michaelle*, while continuing as host for other programs.

- Michaelle Jean was born in Haiti in 1957. At the age of ten, she and her family fled the dictator regime in Haiti to settle in Quebec, Canada.

- When Radio-Canada hired her in 1988, Michaelle started working as a reporter, later becoming the host of programs such as *The Passionate Eye* and *Rough Cuts*, which broadcast the best Canadian and foreign documentary films.

- In 2005, Michaelle was appointed Governor General, becoming the first black woman to represent the Queen for Canada.

- She studied language and literature at the University of Montreal and, from 1984 to 1986, taught Italian Studies while completing a Master of Arts degree in comparative literature.

- Not long after her studies, Michaelle helped establish a network of shelters for women and children across the country, and worked in organizations that helped new immigrants.

_____

_____

_____

_____

_____

_____

_____

_____

_____

_____

_____

_____

_____

_____

_____

D.   Write a narrative paragraph on a topic of your own.

Order of Narration:

1. _____

2. _____

3. _____

4. _____

_____

_____

_____

_____

_____

_____

_____

_____

_____

Politics in Canada

What is *politics*? It is sometimes described as the "art and science of government". It is the way decisions are made among a small group of people that affect larger groups of people. In democratic societies like Canada, we believe that everyone should have a say in such decisions. However, it is easy to see how it can be very difficult to reach agreements this way.

So, in Canada, we have a system of party politics. When elections are called, voters can look at the beliefs and promises, called a "party platform", that each party says it will uphold. The voters may use this to help them decide which candidates to vote for, although they may also decide how to vote based on the individual people running, not the parties they belong to. There are many political parties in Canada. At the moment, the main ones are the Conservative Party, the Liberal Party, the New Democratic Party, the Green Party, and the Bloc Québécois, which is a party that is popular in Quebec, whose main objective is for Quebec to become a separate country.

There are different levels of government. There is the federal, or national, level, for which we elect Members of Parliament (MPs) who meet in Ottawa. There are provincial and territorial governments, for which we elect Members of the Legislative Assembly (MLAs), Members of the House of Assembly (MHAs), Members of the National Assembly (MNAs), or Members of the Provincial Parliament (MPPs), depending on the province or territory. These are people who meet in the capital city of each province or territory in which they are elected. Finally, there is government at the level of cities and municipalities, for which we elect city councillors, mayors, reeves, school board trustees, etc.

No system of government is perfect, and sometimes it seems that few people are happy with it. One way of improving the system is for more women to get involved in politics. There are very few women currently holding public office. It is also important for young people to know they have the right to be a part of government. Adults are used to hearing young people say they want to be firefighters, teachers, or artists when they grow up. Next time someone asks what you want to be, why not tell them you want to be the mayor of your town, the premier of your province, or even the prime minister of Canada? You never know, that dream may actually become reality.

A. List Canada's main political parties. Then write what the terms stand for.

1. The main political parties in Canada:

   _____   _____

   _____   _____

   _____

2. MPs: _____

   MLAs: _____

   MHAs: _____

   MNAs: _____

   MPPs: _____

B. Check the correct sentences and put a cross for the wrong ones.

1. A party platform is the same thing as an election. ☐

2. There are three levels of government in Canada. ☐

3. MPs meet in the capital city of Canada. ☐

4. MLAs, MHAs, MNAs, and MPPs all meet in Toronto. ☐

5. The mayor is elected in a municipal election. ☐

6. The goal of the Bloc Québécois is to keep Quebec united with the rest of Canada. ☐

7. The Bloc Québécois is increasingly popular in provinces outside Quebec. ☐

8. A democratic society has the perfect form of government. ☐

9. Encouraging more women and young people to get involved in politics may improve the way we are governed. ☐

Creating Stories (1)

We use descriptive and narrative writing to create **stories**. To create a good story, we need to make an **outline**:

· Choose from a list of titles or come up with your own.
· Think of the setting – What is the time? What is the place?
· List the events in your story in chronological order.
· Write an ending that either wraps up your story or makes the reader think.

C. **Create a story outline from one of these titles.**

The Strangest Thing that Ever Occurred
A Friendship that Came Out of a Fight
How Bill Became the Funniest Kid at School
Goodbye, Mrs. Wallis

Title: _____

Setting: _____

_____

Events: _____

_____

_____

_____

_____

_____

Ending: _____

_____

_____

Creating Stories (2)

The **introductory paragraph**:
· sets up your story; usually includes the setting

The **body paragraphs**:
· contain details of the events; full of descriptive writing

The **concluding paragraph**:
· either gives a solution or leaves questions unanswered

D. **Write your story based on your outline in (C).**

Title: _____

Introduction: _____

_____

_____

_____

_____

Body: _____

_____

_____

_____

_____

_____

_____

_____

Conclusion: _____

_____

_____

_____

Pierre Laporte

If you drive to Québec City from the southern shore of the St. Lawrence River, chances are, you will drive across *Pont Pierre-Laporte* (Pierre Laporte Bridge). This bridge is the longest main span suspension bridge in Canada. It is more than a kilometre in length, with the central span being 667.5 metres. When viewed alongside the much older Quebec Bridge a short distance downriver, Pierre Laporte Bridge looks like an elegant piece of architecture, and still very modern-looking despite the fact that it was built almost 45 years ago in 1970. But more important for us to remember is the man for whom this bridge is named.

Pierre Laporte was born in Montreal on February 25, 1921. When he was 24 years old, he got a job as a reporter for *Le Devoir*, a major French Canadian newspaper. As a journalist, he was very outspoken about the government of Quebec, and about various politicians. So, it is no surprise that Laporte decided to become a politician himself. He wanted to do something about the problems he saw and not simply write about them. He was elected to the Quebec National Assembly and worked under Premier Jean Lesage. In 1969, Laporte ran for the leadership of the Quebec Liberal Party, but was defeated by Robert Bourassa, who became premier in 1970. Bourassa made Laporte his Vice-Premier and Minister of Labour.

On October 10, 1970, terrorists kidnapped Pierre Laporte, and also James Cross, a British Trade Commissioner stationed in Montreal. These terrorists belonged to a group called *Front de Libération du Québec* (Quebec Liberation Front). This period of time became known as the "October Crisis". It was then that Prime Minister Pierre Trudeau invoked the War Measures Act as a precautionary measure against further terrorist acts.

Pierre Laporte was assassinated. His body was found on October 17. James Cross was held captive for two months and then released. Pierre Laporte is interred in the *Cimetiere Notre-Dame-des-Neiges* in Montreal. Several schools across Canada have also been named in his honour.

A. **Put these events in order. Write 1 to 6.**

Pierre Laporte...

_____ was a journalist for a French Canadian newspaper.

_____ became the name of an elegant bridge in Canada.

_____ was elected to the Quebec National Assembly.

_____ was defeated in his run for the Quebec Liberal Party leadership.

_____ was kidnapped by terrorists, along with a British diplomat.

_____ was Minister of Labour for Robert Bourassa's government.

B. **Give your opinions.**

1. Every job has its own rewards and risks. Do you think Pierre Laporte knew about the risks of his job? What made his work worthwhile despite the danger involved?

    _____

    _____

    _____

2. If you were Pierre Laporte, would you have wanted to become a politician to affect change or would you have kept working as a reporter? Explain.

    _____

    _____

    _____

3. What do you think happened to the kidnappers? If they had served their sentences and are now free, do you think it is fair? Explain.

    _____

    _____

    _____

Writing Suspense

We use **suspense writing** when we want to create **tension** in a story. This type of writing is often used to tell a mystery. Here are examples of techniques to use:

· characters encountering the unknown
· characters experiencing moments of doubt and/or confusion
· characters working against a deadline

C. **Read this piece of suspense and explain how it uses the following techniques.**

Adrian is in the library. He is sitting in front of the computer writing a report on the history of the Pierre Laporte Bridge. Suddenly, the lights go out. He does not know who did it or why. Adrian looks at his watch: 8:15 p.m. It is very late. Adrian calls out for help but there is no one left in the library and the librarian is probably on her break. Quickly he gets up and starts walking but it is so dark that he cannot see the door. He touches the walls, the bookcases, and the tables to help guide himself to the exit. He has to leave right now or he might get locked inside. It is Friday, so if Adrian does not get out in time, he might be stuck inside the library for the whole weekend.

1. **The unknown:**

   _____

   _____

2. **Moments of confusion:**

   _____

   _____

3. **Deadline:**

   _____

   _____

D. **Create your own piece of suspense. First make an outline of your techniques. Below are additional techniques to choose from.**

· characters experiencing something out of the ordinary
· characters involved in a conflict
· characters given a misleading clue

Technique one: _____

_____

_____

Technique two: _____

_____

_____

Technique three: _____

_____

_____

_____

_____

_____

_____

_____

_____

_____

Urbanization

Do you know what "urban sprawl" is? It happens when cities and towns expand, pushing more and more buildings and roads into the countryside. Urbanization is a part of our world, and people lament the fact that we cannot enjoy the pleasures of nature as easily as we were once able to.

Nowadays, many people in Canada are leaving their farms and their homes in the countryside because Canada has become one of the most urbanized countries in the world. It has become very difficult to make a living outside of cities.

Ethelwyn Wetherald was a well-known Canadian poet and journalist, born in Rockwood, Ontario in 1857. Much of what she wrote was about nature and family life. She loved the natural world and understood, even in her day, that there was an unhealthy side to "progress". Imagine what she would think if she were alive today.

Children in the City [1]
by Ethelwyn Wetherald (1857-1940)

Thousands of childish ears, rough chidden,
Never a sweet bird-note have heard;
Deep in the leafy woodland hidden
Dies, unlistened to, many a bird.
For small soiled hands in the sordid city
Blossoms open and die unbreathed;
For feet unwashed by the tears of pity
Streams around meadows of green are wreathed.

Warm, unrevelled in, still they wander,
Summer breezes out in the fields;
Scarcely noticed, the green months squander
All the wealth that the summer yields.
Ah, the pain of it! Ah, the pity!
Opulent stretch the country skies
Over solitudes, while in the city
Starving for beauty are childish eyes.

[1] *From Library and Archives Canada*

A. **Use your own words to explain the following verses.**

1. Thousands of childish ears, rough chidden,
   Never a sweet bird-note have heard;
   Deep in the leafy woodland hidden
   Dies, unlistened to, many a bird.

   _____

   _____

   _____

2. Scarcely noticed, the green months squander
   All the wealth that the summer yields.

   _____

   _____

3. What do you think "solitudes" means in the following?

   Opulent stretch the country skies
   Over solitudes, while in the city
   Starving for beauty are childish eyes.

   _____

   _____

   _____

B. **There is an unhealthy side to "progress". Explain in a paragraph how this can be true. Use examples to support your writing.**

_____

_____

_____

_____

_____

26

Literary Devices (1)

To write creatively, we can use a **literary device** called **personification**, which gives human qualities to inanimate things.

Example: The music danced in the room.

C.   Check the lines where personification is used.

1.   Ah, the pain of it! Ah, the pity!   ____

2.   Deep in the leafy woodland dies many a bird.   ____

3.   Starving for beauty are childish eyes.   ____

4.   Streams are wreathed around meadows of green.   ____

5.   The green months squander all the summer yields.   ____

D.   Complete these sentences with verbs that personify the inanimate objects.

1.   The violets _____ in a field of green.

2.   The falling leaves _____ in the autumn air.

3.   The dripping wet cloth _____ while the creaking floor
_____ .

4.   The present is where the future _____ into the past.

5.   My pack of Skittles ended up _____ the kitchen floor when
I opened it the wrong way.

6.   That heavy apple is _____ into the
soft grass below.

7.   "Look," says Madeline. "These
peaches are so shy that they

are _____ ."

Literary Devices (2)

Besides personification, we can also use similes and metaphors to make our writing more creative. A **simile** is a comparison of two things with characteristics in common. A **metaphor** is a comparison as well, but without using "as" or "like". When using a metaphor, we are describing something as though it were something else.

Examples: Sara dresses up like the northern lights. (simile)
Sara is the northern lights. (metaphor)

E.   Use similes or metaphors to make these sentences more creative. You may change some words in the sentences if necessary.

1.   The sun rose slowly in the east.

_____

2.   The little girl scurried into her room.

_____

3.   Elena was so worn out after her train ride.

_____

4.   Mrs. Fields bakes good cookies.

_____

5.   Grace glanced down at her watch.

_____

6.   James dashed into the classroom.

_____

7.   The mid-autumn rain splattered on the roof.

_____

Andrew Barton "Banjo" Patterson is Australia's favourite poet. He wrote many poems in his lifetime, including "The Man from Snowy River". But his best-known poem, familiar around the world and put to a song, is "Waltzing Matilda". Many Australians would like this poem to be Australia's national anthem (the current anthem is "Advance Australia Fair").

It helps to know a few Australian English words before you read this poem:

- a swagman: a hobo or travelling sheep shearer
- a billabong: a watering hole
- a billy: a tin can
- a jumbuck: a sheep
- a tucker bag: a food bag
- a squatter: a station ranch owner

Waltzing **Matilda**

There is some debate as to what "Waltzing Matilda" really means, but some say it means to live the free life, like a swagman.

Waltzing Matilda

OH! There once was a swagman camped in the Billabong,
Under the shade of a Coolabah tree;
And he sang as he looked at the old billy boiling,
"Who'll come a-waltzing Matilda with me."

Who'll come a-waltzing Matilda, my darling,
Who'll come a-waltzing Matilda with me?
Waltzing Matilda and leading a water-bag –
Who'll come a-waltzing Matilda with me?

Down came a jumbuck to drink at the billabong.
Up jumped the swagman and grabbed him with glee,
And he said as he put him away in the tucker bag
"You'll come a-waltzing Matilda with me!"

Down came the Squatter a-riding his thoroughbred.
Down came Policemen – one, two, and three.
"Whose is the jumbuck you've got in the tucker bag?
You'll come a-waltzing Matilda with me."

But the swagman, he up and he jumped in the water-hole,
Drowning himself by the Coolabah tree;
And his ghost may be heard as it sings by the Billabong,
"Who'll come a-waltzing Matilda with me?"

A.   Circle "T" for the true sentences and "F" for the false ones.

1.   "Waltzing Matilda" used to be the national anthem of Australia.   T   F

2.   The words of "Waltzing Matilda" were written by a poet.   T   F

3.   Some say that "Waltzing Matilda" actually means dancing kangaroos.   T   F

4.   A swagman is a travelling sheep shearer.   T   F

5.   A jumbuck is a food bag.   T   F

6.   The Australian anthem is "Advance Australia Fair".   T   F

B.   Write your own responses.

1.   What is your idea of a free life? Briefly describe.

_____

_____

_____

_____

_____

2.   Australians have strong empathy for this song, partly because it features an "anti-hero". Look up the meaning of this word. Why might an anti-hero be unpopular in real life, but draw sympathy when featured in songs, novels, or films?

_____

_____

_____

_____

_____

Mood (1)

The **mood** of a piece of writing affects the reader's emotions. It may be **cheerful**, **humorous**, **sad**, **serious**, **light-hearted**, etc. It may remain constant or change throughout. Here are examples of techniques for creating mood:

- word choice (e.g. types of adjectives and verbs used)
- sensory details (i.e. sight, hearing, taste, smell, touch)
- literary devices (e.g. personification, similes, metaphors, rhyme)

C. **Read these verses and see how different moods are created.**

1. Who'll come a-waltzing Matilda, <u>my darling</u>,
   Who'll come a-waltzing Matilda with me?
   Waltzing Matilda and leading a water-bag –
   Who'll come a-waltzing Matilda with me?

   Mood: light-hearted

   Technique: word choice
                my darling

2. Down came a jumbuck to drink at the billabong.
   Up jumped the swagman and grabbed him with <u>glee</u>,
   And he said as he put him away in the tucker bag
   <u>"You'll come a-waltzing Matilda with me!"</u>

   Mood: humorous

   Techniques: 1) word choice
               glee

               2) literary device (personification)
               The sheep will go "a-waltzing" Matilda with the swagman.

D. **Identify the moods and the techniques used to create them in these verses.**

1. Down came the Squatter a-riding his thoroughbred.
   <u>Down came Policemen – one, two, and three.</u>
   "Whose is the jumbuck you've got in the tucker bag?
   You'll come a-waltzing Matilda with me."

   Mood: _____

   Technique: _____

2. But the swagman, he up and he jumped in the water-hole,
   Drowning himself by the Coolabah tree;
   <u>And his ghost may be heard as it sings by the billabong,</u>
   "Who'll come a-waltzing Matilda with me?"

   Mood: _____

   Technique: _____

E. **Think of a mood you want to create. Use one of the techniques to create it in a short poem.**

_____

_____

_____

_____

_____

_____

New School, New Life

Dear Diary,

I start my first day of school at junior high today! I can't believe that this day has finally arrived. It seems like I have been thinking about it all summer.

I have to admit that a lot of what I have been thinking about makes me nervous. After all, I was one of the leaders at my old school. The younger students all looked up to us sixth graders. Now, I'm going to be a new kid all over again, and I'm going to have to make new friends...

At least I'm not alone. All of us going into junior high are in the same boat, like Grandma says, so that makes it fair. In fact, when I'm not worrying about being a new junior high school student, I'm excited about it! I'm excited about all the different subjects I get to study. We even have a class on religion at my new school. I'm excited about learning to speak Mandarin too.

The letter I got last week from my new school says that this Friday will be Club Day. There are a lot of clubs at my new school. I think I might join the Karate Club and the Filmmaking Club. Dad told me that a good way to make new friends is to meet people who share your hobbies.

I know I will miss my old friends when I'm in this new school, but I know there will be at least three other students from my elementary school. I also know that I can still stay in touch with my old buddies even if we no longer go to the same school. It's up to us to make the effort.

I'm so excited now! Mom, Dad, Grandma, and Grandpa are all excited for me as well. I think I'm going to like being a junior high school student after all. I'm looking forward to a great year — and an exciting new world!

Gotta go. Mom is calling from downstairs. She wants to take a picture of me before I head out. Sheesh!

A. Write your thoughts.

1. "Now, I'm going to be a new kid all over again, and I'm going to have to make new friends..." What is it about new things that makes us all a little nervous? Give an example of your own experience.

_____

_____

_____

_____

2. What do you think the narrator will learn from his class on religion? How do you think it will benefit him?

_____

_____

_____

_____

3. "A good way to make new friends is to meet people who share your hobbies." Support this sentence with an example of your own.

_____

_____

_____

_____

4. Do you have friends who have completely different hobbies from you? If so, what keeps you together? If not, why not?

_____

_____

_____

_____

Mood (2)

Mood can be described in colours or shades of light, such as **grey**, **bright**, and **dark**. We can change the mood of a paragraph by changing the words, sensory details, and/or literary devices used.

B. Read the first paragraph and circle the words describing its mood. Then read the next paragraph and see how the mood is changed. Circle the words describing the new mood.

The new school is a red building flanked by a gently sloping field, like a castle on a hill. As soon as the bell rings for recess, boys and girls rush out of their classrooms, brushing the dandelions as they spend their next 15 minutes outside. Some play dodge ball, some play catch, some huddle into groups to chat, and some simply run around, laughing and squeaking under the sun. The bell rings again, and the children rush to line up in front of the building – albeit a little reluctantly – to return to their classrooms on this fine Friday afternoon.

1. Mood: sad / light-hearted / humorous / serious / bright

The new school is a grey building flanked by a sloping field, like an abandoned castle on a hill. As soon as the bell rings for recess, boys and girls haul themselves out of their classrooms, stomping through the snow as they spend their next 15 minutes outside. Some build snow fortresses, some try to run in the field, some huddle into groups to stay warm, and some simply wander around, quiet and lonely amid the snow. The bell rings again, and the children haul themselves back to line up in front of the building – as if it were a daily ritual – to return to their classrooms on this bleak winter morning.

2. Mood: grey / light-hearted / humorous / sad / serious

C. **Create a mood in a paragraph and write down all the words describing this mood. Then change its mood in another paragraph and write down the words describing this new mood.**

_____

_____

_____

_____

_____

_____

_____

_____

Mood : _____

_____

_____

_____

_____

_____

_____

_____

_____

Mood : _____

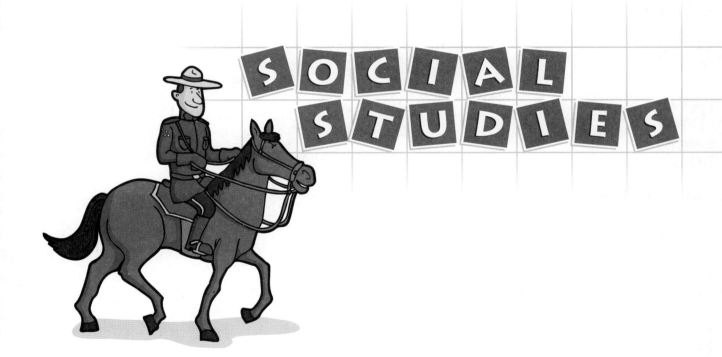

SOCIAL STUDIES

NEW HOME

The Founding Nations of Canada

Long before the British and the French explorers came and settled in what is now Canada, Indigenous Peoples had already lived on this land. They, together with the British and the French, have been referred to by the Canadian government as the founding nations of Canada.

A. **Fill in the blanks to complete the sentences about the beliefs of the founding nations of Canada.**

Indigenous Peoples   Catholic   British   societal
colonies   individual   natural   parliament

The Founding Nations of Canada

First Peoples   The First Peoples
French   The French
British   The British

Spiritual Beliefs

First Peoples Beliefs were centred around the Great Spirit and the 1.＿＿＿＿＿＿＿＿ environment.

French The 2.＿＿＿＿＿＿＿ religion was the main religion in New France.

British Every 3.＿＿＿＿＿＿＿ can have a personal relationship with God.

Political Beliefs

First Peoples Political policies must have 4.＿＿＿＿＿＿＿ consensus before they are applied.

French The 5.＿＿＿＿＿＿＿ were a significant threat.

British The monarch governs the society with the guidance of the 6.＿＿＿＿＿＿＿ , which must be supreme.

Economic Beliefs

First Peoples Gains and benefits from trade should be shared by all members of the community.

French Trade relations with the 7.＿＿＿＿＿＿＿ had to be maintained.

British The 8.＿＿＿＿＿＿＿ should serve the interest of Britain.

B. Identify what the founding nations contributed to the development of Canada. Write the letters and give one more example for each. Then answer the question.

A TEK (Traditional Ecological Knowledge) of using natural resources sustainably for survival

> *The three founding nations, with their early beliefs and contributions, played a vital role in shaping Canada's identity.*

B the image of the Queen on Canadian coins

C bilingualism, with English and French as the official languages

D traditional herbal medicine for healing the body and the mind

E canoes for travelling along difficult waterways

F parliamentary system; court and law systems

G French education across the country

H survival tactics for the harsh winters, like using animal fur to keep warm

I helping the British repel the invading American forces in the War of 1812

J Canada as a constitutional monarchy, with the Queen as the head of state

K English-speaking majority in Canada

What the Founding Nations Contributed to Canada

The First Peoples

Contributions: _____

My example: _____

The French

Contributions: _____

My example: _____

The British

Contributions: _____

My example: _____

Which one of the above do you think contributed most to Canada's identity? Why?

_____

_____

Immigration to Canada

Canada is known as the "land of immigrants". Ever since the French and British explorers came to explore its land and settle here, people from across the globe have chosen to make Canada their new home for different reasons.

A. Unscramble the letters to see why people in the past left their homeland and immigrated to Canada.

Canada's Early Settlers and Immigrants

In the late 15ᵗʰ and 16ᵗʰ centuries, the French and the British came to what was to be Canada to explore new 1._____ (aldn) and build 2._____ (loconeis).

In the early 18ᵗʰ century, the Black Loyalists left the British colonies in America and came to Canada to escape the American Revolution, persecution, and 3._____ (veslray). They were promised land, rights, and 4._____ (eeomdfr). They were also promised 5._____ (arifmng) tools, 6._____ (dofo), and clothing for two years.

Later, in the 19ᵗʰ century, Irish immigrants sought refuge in Canada from 7._____ (amifne), 8._____ (perovty), and 9._____ (sesedias). They worked on the development of canals in Canada. A large number of Chinese immigrants also came for the 10._____ (bjo) opportunities in gold mines and with the Canadian Pacific Railway project. Immigrants from other countries also came to escape 11._____ (raws) in their homeland.

B. **Write the letters in the boxes to complete the timeline. Then answer the question.**

Timeline of the Immigration History of Canada

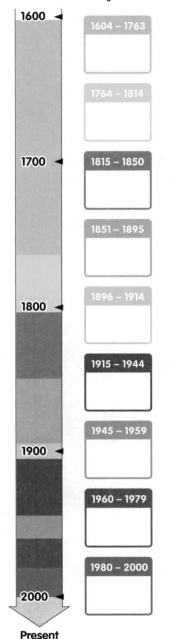

1600

1604 – 1763

1764 – 1814

1700

1815 – 1850

1851 – 1895

1896 – 1914

1800

1915 – 1944

1945 – 1959

1900

1960 – 1979

1980 – 2000

2000

Present

A After the First World War (1914 – 1918) and the Great Depression, there were immigration restrictions on people of certain heritage. The number of immigrants dropped.

B The Canadian Multiculturalism Act was passed in 1988, encouraging people from all over the world to immigrate to Canada.

C Between 1868 and 1964, because of deteriorating living conditions in Britain, about 100 000 British children were sent to live in Canadian foster homes. From 1881 to 1884, many Chinese immigrants came to work on the construction of the Canadian Pacific Railway.

D In the late 19th and early 20th centuries, free land was offered to encourage immigrants from Europe and the United States.

E The French built settlements in New France in 1604.

F British immigrants, mostly Irish immigrants escaping the Great Famine that began in 1845 in Ireland, came.

G After the Second World War (1939 – 1945), immigration was encouraged, and Canada accepted many European refugees.

H Between 1783 and 1784, a large number of loyalists came to Canada, fleeing the oppression of the American Revolution.

I The "Point System" was introduced in 1967 to assess the qualifications of immigrants.

When did your community members first come to Canada? Where did they settle and why did they settle there?

_____

_____

3

Home Children in Canada

NEW HOME

In the late 19th century, British Home Children were sent to live in Canada. They came from similar backgrounds but ended up leading very different lives. Canadians have had different opinions on this child migration scheme.

A. Fill in the blanks to complete the passage about the Home Children.

2010   farms   descendants
exploited   domestic
labour   orphaned   adopted

British Home Children in Canada

Beginning in the late 19th century, more than 100 000 poor, abandoned, and 1._____ children from Britain were shipped to Canada. This was done with the initial intention of helping the children and providing cheap farm 2._____ and 3._____ help for rural Canadian families. These children were known as Home Children.

I am British. I am going to Canada.

While some of these Home Children were lucky enough to be 4._____ and live better lives in Canada, others were 5._____ and abused. They led harsh lives, working mostly on 6._____ from dawn till dusk. Their contributions were acknowledged by the Canadian government when it declared 7._____ the year of the British Home Child. Today, it is estimated that about 11% of Canadians are 8._____ of these Home Children.

B. **Read the opinions of two Canadians on the Home Children. Answer the questions.**

"Canadians don't expect their government to apologize for every sad event in our history...the reality is that here in Canada we are taking measures to recognize that sad period, but there is, I think, limited public interest in official government apologies for everything that's ever been unfortunate..."

Jason Kenney
Immigration Minister 2009

"We've got four million Canadians who are descendants of the Home Children and I think they deserve an apology for what their parents went through...they didn't want money. They just wanted an apology and to find where they came from."

Sidney Baker
Spokesperson for
Home Children Canada

Whom do you agree with? Why?

_____

_____

_____

Canada Post released a special stamp in 2010 to honour the Home Children. Suggest one more way in which Canadians can acknowledge the contributions and hardships of the Home Children.

_____

_____

NEW HOME

The Chinese Canadians

The Chinese population is one of the largest ethnic groups in Canada. It has contributed greatly to Canadian history and continues to be an important part of its society today.

A. **Look at the timeline of the history of Chinese people in Canada. Identify the reasons for the events. Then answer the question.**

History of Chinese People in Canada

	Reason	Event
late 1850s	☐	— immigration of the Chinese to British Columbia
1881 – 1884	☐	— influx of Chinese workers
1885	☐	— imposition of the head tax under the Chinese Immigration Act
1923	☐	— implementation of the Chinese Exclusion Act
1947	☐	— repeal of the Chinese Exclusion Act and other discriminatory laws against the Chinese
2006	☐	— official apology for the mistreatment of the Chinese people from the prime minister on behalf of the Canadian government

Present

Ⓐ to recognize the injustice and discrimination of the head tax and the Chinese Exclusion Act

Ⓑ to dig for gold in the Fraser Canyon Gold Rush in British Columbia

Ⓒ to prohibit the Chinese from immigrating to Canada

Ⓓ to recognize Chinese Canadians' participation and contributions during World War II

Ⓔ to help in the construction of the Canadian Pacific Railway (CPR)

Ⓕ to discourage the Chinese from entering or settling in Canada after the completion of the CPR

What effect did the Chinese head tax have on Chinese immigrants in Canada and their families back in their home country?

_____

_____

B. Fill in the blanks to complete the paragraphs about the contributions of the Chinese people to the growth of Canada.

> economic   invest   businesses   sacrifices
> trade   community   patriotism   ethic

Since their arrival in Canada, the Chinese have greatly benefited the country. The completion of the Canadian Pacific Railway (CPR) ahead of schedule could only be achieved with the hard work and 1._____ made by the Chinese workers. The CPR connects Canada from coast to coast and makes it possible to 2._____ and travel across the country.

Chinese war veterans fought for Canada and demonstrated their 3._____ to Canada during World War II. In addition, since World War II, many Chinese Canadians have set up small and medium-sized 4._____ . They have a strong business sense and are willing to 5._____ and take risks. They, together with other well-educated Chinese immigrants who have used their skills and knowledge to work here, have greatly contributed to the 6._____ growth of Canada.

The Chinese community also reflects and strengthens Canadian values through their strong work 7._____ , integration in society, and commitment to family and 8._____ values.

The Japanese Canadians

The Japanese Canadians have endured a lot of hardships, particularly their forced relocation during World War II, to achieve their current status in Canada. The Japanese Canadians and the government have held different perspectives on this event over the years.

A. Match the effects with the causes. Write the letters.

Cause

From 1877 to 1928, the first wave of Japanese immigrants settled in British Columbia. They made a living mainly by fishing and farming.

Effect
1.

Cause

The Japanese immigrants were excluded from Canadian society.

Effect
2.

Cause

In 1941, Japan attacked the U.S. naval base at Pearl Harbour, Hawaii.

Effect
3.

Cause

In 1945, the British government wanted to recruit Japanese Canadians as interpreters for the British forces.

Effect
4.

Cause

The Japanese Canadians fought for an apology and redress for their losses due to their forced internment and relocation.

Effect
5.

EFFECT

A The federal government enlisted 119 second-generation Japanese as interpreters in the Canadian Intelligence Corps.

B Racist attitudes among the Canadians already settled there started to develop as they thought that their livelihoods were threatened.

C The Japanese Canadians developed their own community with various social, economic, and religious institutions.

D In 1988, Prime Minister Brian Mulroney apologized on behalf of the federal government for their wrongdoing to the Japanese Canadians during and after World War II.

E The federal government used the War Measures Act to relocate the Japanese Canadians to road camps and internment camps, and later to areas away from the west coast. All their property was confiscated at the time of relocation.

B. **Match the people with their viewpoints on the forced relocation of the Japanese Canadians. Then answer the question.**

Ⓐ We cannot change the past. But we must, as a nation, have the courage to face up to these historical facts...I speak for Members on all sides of the House today in offering to Japanese Canadians the formal and sincere apology of this Parliament for those past injustices against them, against their families, and against their heritage, and our solemn commitment and undertaking to Canadians of every origin that such violations will never again in this country be countenanced or repeated.

Ⓑ Born in Canada...I had perceived myself to be as Canadian as the beaver...I had committed no crime. I was never charged, tried, or convicted of anything. Yet I was fingerprinted and interned.

Ⓒ The sound policy and the best policy for the Japanese Canadians themselves is to distribute widely as possible throughout the country where they will not create feelings of racial hostility.

Ⓓ It is the government's plan to get these people out of B.C. as fast as possible...Let our slogan be for British Columbia: No Japs from the Rockies to the seas.

Mackenzie King
Prime Minister, 1944

Ken Adachi
Japanese Canadian, 1988

Brian Mulroney
Prime Minister, 1988

Ian Alistair Mackenzie
Federal Cabinet Minister, 1944

Whose viewpoint do you support? Why?

_____

_____

_____

The Demolition of Africville

Africville was a small community in Nova Scotia. Its former site was designated a National Historic Site of Canada in 1996. Africville is known as a symbol of African-Canadians' struggle against racism.

A. Fill in the blanks to complete the paragraphs about Africville.

| apologized | renewal | church | Black Loyalists | Halifax |
| dump | replica | utilities | protests | undesirable | industrial |

Africville was a small community on the land granted by the British to the 1._____ in the 19ᵗʰ century. It was located on the Bedford Basin in northwestern 2._____ , Nova Scotia. It had been home to hundreds of African Nova Scotians for more than 150 years.

Residents of Africville had to pay municipal taxes, but they did not get the basic 3._____ such as water, sewage, electricity, and street lights, or police and fire services from the city of Halifax. Instead, the city built 4._____ facilities, including a prison, an infectious disease hospital, a slaughterhouse, and even the city garbage 5._____ in the Africville community.

In the 1960s, Africville was demolished in the name of urban 6._____ and 7._____ development despite protests and resistance. The residents were uprooted and relocated to their new "homes" in dump trucks. Their houses were bulldozed and their 8._____ , which was the heart of the community, was torn down.

In the 1980s, the central area of the site of Africville became Seaview Memorial Park, where former residents and their descendants carried out 9._____ throughout the 1980s and 1990s. In 2010, the city officially 10._____ to former residents of Africville. A 11._____ of their church was built in 2011 as promised and the area was renamed Africville Park.

B. An Africville resident and a Halifax city councillor would have had very different viewpoints on the demolition of Africville. Determine what each of them would have said. Write the letters in the speech bubbles.

Ⓐ Job training, employment assistance, and education programs will be provided.

Ⓑ We will lose our homes, our businesses, and our livelihood.

Ⓒ We have your best interests at heart. Your living conditions will improve.

Ⓓ There will be free lawyers and social workers available to help you.

Ⓔ The financial compensation cannot make up for our emotional suffering.

Ⓕ You will get a $500 payment and a furniture allowance.

Ⓖ We are a close-knit community. We belong here. We won't have the same sense of belonging toward a new place.

Ⓗ Destroying our homes means depriving us of our dignity.

The better living conditions and employment and education programs promised by the city of Halifax to the residents of Africville never materialized. If you were a descendant of former Africville residents, would you be satisfied with the official apology from the city and the rebuilding of the church? Why or why not?

_____

_____

7

The Image of Canada

The image of Canada is shaped by its long history and diverse cultures. There are many unique symbols that represent who we are and what we stand for today.

A. Name the symbols of Canada. Then answer the question.

Symbols of Canada

1. Canada's national summer sport

    _____

2. home to Canada's federal government

    _____

3. flies on all government buildings

    _____

4. symbol of the fur trade, which is an important part of Canadian history

    _____

5. representing the strong agricultural heritage of the Prairies

    _____

There is an animal symbol that represents the strength, courage, intelligence, persistence, and resilience that Canadians value. Do you know what it is?

6. _____

B. **In your opinion, rate what people around the world think of Canada. Then answer the question.**

What People around the World Think of Canada

	least describes Canada				best describes Canada
	1	**2**	**3**	**4**	**5**
1. It is freezing cold.					
2. It has pristine nature and diverse landscapes.					
3. People are friendly, genteel, and generous.					
4. People are open-minded.					
5. It is multicultural.					
6. Many people speak French.					
7. It has a low crime rate.					
8. It has a good health care system.					
9. It has a good education system.					
10. It provides the best quality of life.					

Look at the symbols in (A) again and what people think about Canada above. How would you describe Canada?

_____

_____

_____

_____

Multiculturalism in Canada

Canada is a country that accepts people of all races, languages, and religions. Everyone has the right to preserve his or her own culture and traditions. Many unique communities, for example, the Mennonites, have contributed to Canada's multicultural identity.

A. **Name the communities. Then identify what the people from the communities say. Write the letters.**

Muslim   Jewish
Irish   Mennonite

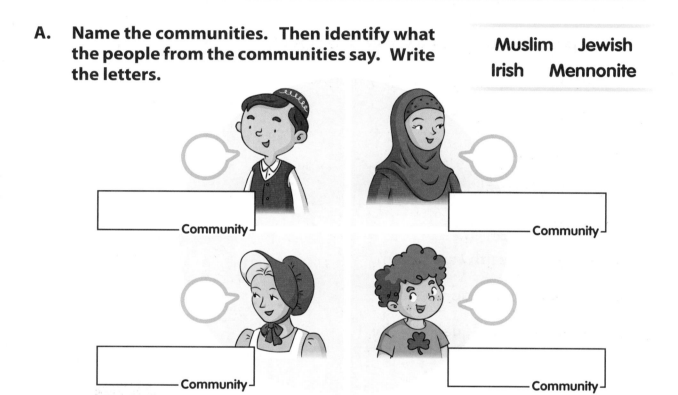

Community

Community

Community

Community

Ⓐ We make up 15% of Canada's population. Step dancing is an important part of our culture. The Catholics in our community celebrate St. Patrick's Day. We wear green clothing on this day.

Ⓑ The mosque is our place of worship. We celebrate the religious festival of Eid al-Fitr, which marks the end of a month-long fast. The women in our community wear "hijabs" (scarves that cover the head and neck) in schools and workplaces.

Ⓒ We observe kosher practices. Passover and Hanukkah, which is also known as the Festival of Lights, are two of our major festivals. The men in our community wear "kippahs", which are small skullcaps, as a gesture of piety and respect when they pray.

Ⓓ We are an isolated community. We live traditional farm lives in rural areas. Women wear long plain dresses with bonnets and men wear straw hats. Children go to schools run by our own community.

B. **Fill in the blanks to learn more about the Canadian Mennonites. Then complete the chart with information from (A) and (B).**

The Canadian Mennonites

Waterloo   buggies   religious
technology   ethnic   military

The Canadian Mennonites are Christian communities with members of different 1._____ origins. They have lived in Canada since the late 18th century. Early Mennonites came because they were promised 2._____ freedom, cheap or free farmland, and exemption from 3._____ service.

Today, while many Mennonites live urban lives and are not easily distinguishable from the rest of society, the Old Order Mennonites, like those living in 4._____ , Ontario, lead very traditional lifestyles. They wear plain, simple clothing. They avoid using modern 5._____ and electricity. They use old-fashioned methods and simple machinery to farm. Instead of driving motor vehicles, they use horses and 6._____ for transportation. Their unique culture and traditions contribute to Canada's multiculturalism.

Comparing the Old Order Mennonite Community and Your Community:

	Old Order Mennonite Community	My Community
Religion	_____	_____
Clothing	_____	_____
Use of Technology	_____	_____
Means of Transport	_____	_____
Education	_____	_____

9

Ethnic Neighbourhoods

Many new immigrants to Canada prefer to live in ethnic neighbourhoods where they find comfort and support from people of the same ethnic origin. However, some Canadians have a different opinion on the formation of ethnic neighbourhoods.

A. Circle the correct words to complete the passage.

Ethnic Neighbourhoods in Canada

An ethnic neighbourhood is formed when a large number of people from a particular ethnic or cultural origin, one that is not the **minority / majority** in the general population, come together to reside or run businesses in a specified area. The people in an ethnic neighbourhood share the same **language / education**, customs, traditions, and, sometimes, religion.

Canada is a multicultural country with people of many different ethnic origins, including Chinese, South Asian, Black, Filipino, Korean, Greek, Italian, and Latin American. The **decline / growth** in immigration has resulted in the formation of many ethnic neighbourhoods. There are Chinatowns, Greektowns, Little Italys, and South Asian neighbourhoods in **small / major** cities such as Toronto, Montreal, and Vancouver. Ethnic neighbourhoods have **canteens / restaurants** that serve authentic ethnic cuisines and specialty shops that sell **traditional / generic** clothing and other items that cater to the needs of the particular ethnic groups.

Vancouver's Chinatown

B. **Identify the perspectives of the two groups of people. Write the letters.**

Perspectives on the Formation of Ethnic Neighbourhoods

(A) Ethnic neighbourhoods provide an opportunity for everyone to learn about different cultures from around the world.

(B) Our ethnic neighbourhoods provide comfort for us because everybody speaks the same language and shares the same cultural values.

(C) Ethnic neighbourhoods differentiate one ethnic group from another. This is not good since Canada wants all cultures to exist in harmony.

(D) Living in the same neighbourhood allows us to feel secure and less threatened by racism and discrimination.

(E) We fear that the unique traditions and cultures of ethnic groups may reshape Canada.

(F) The formation of ethnic neighbourhoods shows that newcomers have no intention of integrating into society and becoming "real Canadians".

(G) Descendants of our ethnic groups have the opportunity to learn about our unique heritage.

(H) Living in ethnic neighbourhoods is a way of integrating into Canada because people from similar backgrounds help one another get jobs and settle in Canada.

(I) When an ethnic neighbourhood expands, existing established residents like us are pushed out of the neighbourhood.

New Immigrants

Some Established Canadians

Support and Inclusiveness

In addition to ethnic communities supporting new immigrants, there are various other groups that make enormous efforts to help people from all backgrounds settle and integrate into society. They contribute to the Canadian identity of inclusiveness.

A.   Identify the groups. Then fill in the blanks.

labour organizations   advocacy organizations for immigrants

1. _____   influence   rights   society   refugees

These organizations are committed to protecting the _____ of immigrants. They work to _____ policies and decisions that involve issues concerning immigrants. One example is the Canadian Council for Refugees, which is a non-profit umbrella organization with member organizations that work to protect and help _____ and immigrants in Canada and around the world in their settlement. They help them become integral members of _____ .

2. _____   equality   bargaining   workforce   workers

These organizations negotiate on behalf of _____ with employers to achieve improvements in pay, benefits, and working conditions through collective _____ . One such organization is the Canadian Labour Congress, which demands human rights and _____ rights for all workers, particularly for Aboriginal workers, young workers, women, workers of colour, and workers with disabilities in the _____ in Canada and from around the world.

B. Read about another group that contributes to the Canadian identity of inclusiveness. Then answer the questions.

L'Arche is an international, non-profit organization founded in 1964 by Canadian humanitarian Jean Vanier based on the belief that every person, including those with developmental disabilities, is valued and can make a contribution. It aims to help and support people with intellectual disabilities and foster the recognition of their contributions to society so that they can be actively integrated into public life.

L'Arche establishes communities of small homes across Canada, where its support assistants of diverse social, cultural, and religious backgrounds live, work, and learn with people with intellectual disabilities in family-like environments. Although they are of different intellectual capacities, they support one another to reach their full potential, and develop self and mutual understanding. They respect one another, develop long-term stable relationships, and become responsible adults. They work together to contribute to their home, community, and society. L'Arche is playing its part in building an open, caring, understanding, and inclusive society in Canada.

1. *How do L'Arche's family-like environments help people with intellectual disabilities?*

   _____

   _____

2. Why do you think it is important for support assistants in L'Arche communities to be of diverse social, cultural, and religious backgrounds?

   _____

   _____

3. Write one way in which L'Arche is contributing to the goal of inclusiveness in Canada.

   _____

   _____

11

Human Rights and Violations

Canada guarantees human rights to all individuals. However, there have been violations of these rights throughout Canada's history and even recently. Laws are made to prevent these violations from happening.

A. Read the passage. Then check the correct items and answer the question.

Human rights are rights that acknowledge the dignity and worth of an individual, and ensure that equal rights and opportunities are available to all without discrimination.

The Charter of Rights and Freedoms (1982) grants basic human rights to everyone, including non-citizens, in Canada. No federal or provincial laws may go against these guaranteed rights and freedoms. The Charter only applies to governments, not to interactions between organizations or between individuals.

At the federal level, the Canadian Human Rights Act protects federal employees and people who receive services from the federal government, the First Nations governments, and companies regulated by the federal government from harassment and discrimination based on race, age, sex, colour, national or ethnic origin, religion, disability, marital and family status, sexual orientation, and a conviction for which a pardon has been granted or a record suspended. There are seven discriminatory practices that are prohibited, among which is paying men and women differently when they are doing work of the same value.

Human rights are also protected by laws and legislation in every province and territory. For example, the Ontario Human Rights Code prohibits discrimination against and harassment of people based on age, ancestry, colour, race, ethnic origin, place of origin, citizenship, disability, family and marital status, creed, gender identity and expression, sex and sexual orientation, record of offences, and receipt of public assistance in social areas including housing, employment, contracts, goods, services, and facilities.

Prohibited Grounds of Discrimination	Canadian Human Rights Act	Ontario Human Rights Code
age and gender	○	○
race and colour	○	○
national and ethnic origin	○	○
marital and family status	○	○
religion and beliefs	○	○
citizenship	○	○
disability	○	○
gender identity and expression	○	○
sexual orientation	○	○
record of offences	○	○
suspended/pardoned conviction	○	○

From the chart, you can see that the Act and the Code have very similar prohibited grounds of discrimination. Describe the main difference between them.

_____

_____

B.   Study the case. Then answer the questions.

Aadil worked in a coffee shop in Niagara Falls. He was mocked and subjected to racist remarks at his workplace for speaking in his native language with some customers. He was also forced to eat in violation of his religious beliefs and was threatened to be replaced with a worker of a different race. When he asserted his right to be free from discrimination, he was fired.

1.   Which law should Aadil turn to for protection against discrimination?

_____

2.   On which grounds was Aadil discriminated against?

_____

_____

12

Income Inequality

Income inequality is an important indicator of the social and economic well-being of a country. The widening income gap between the upper class and the working class in Canada has brought about social and economic differences between the two groups.

A. Read the paragraphs. Then answer the questions.

Income inequality is the uneven distribution of income in a country. A country with high income inequality signifies unequal distribution of wealth, a high unemployment rate, high levels of child poverty and poor health, and even a high crime rate. All of these factors hamper the country's long-term economic growth.

Income inequality in Canada has been increasing. It has led to differences in the social and economic aspects of life between the upper-class and working-class people. Certain groups such as new immigrants, visible minorities, women, and people with lower levels of education can only take up low-wage jobs and they face the possibility of unemployment and exclusion from the majority of society.

In recent years, Canada has tried to solve the problems of income inequality. Its tax and transfer system helps reduce income inequality only slightly, and there is still much more to be done by the Canadian government to resolve this issue.

1. Which groups are negatively affected by income inequality?

   _____

   _____

2. Choose one group that is negatively affected and explain why those people might have low incomes.

   _____

   _____

3. Many people see income inequality as a measure of fairness and social justice. Do you think so? Why?

_____

_____

4. Choose three ways in which you think the Canadian government can most effectively resolve the issue of income inequality.

○ impose higher taxes on corporate profits and high-income earners

○ implement stronger employment laws to boost wages for working-class people

○ provide more support and services for vulnerable groups such as women and new immigrants

○ create more job opportunities

○ reduce GST/HST

B. **Identify the social differences and economic differences.**

Income inequality has led to social and economic differences between upper-class and working-class people in Canada.

Ⓐ Upper-class Canadians earn significantly higher incomes than working-class people.

Ⓑ Working-class people have more health issues.

Ⓒ Working-class Canadians report low levels of job satisfaction.

Ⓓ Upper-class individuals achieve higher levels of education.

Ⓔ Children from working-class families have fewer opportunities to participate in sports and recreational activities outside school.

Ⓕ Working-class people tend to have more difficulties repaying debts.

Ⓖ Upper-class families live in neighbourhoods where houses are bigger and much more expensive.

Social Differences

Economic Differences

13

Canada's Free Trade Agreements

The Canadian government interacts with other countries in various ways. One major way is through free trade agreements.

A. **Fill in the blanks. Then name the countries that have free trade agreements with Canada.**

A free trade agreement (FTA) allows a country to trade goods and 1._____ with one or more partner countries with a reduction or an elimination of 2._____ and other non-tariff barriers like 3._____ . This enables the businesses in the country to stay 4._____ with those of its partner countries.

quotas
services
competitive
tariffs

Canada's Trading Partners

Mexico   Panama   Peru
Chile   Jordan   United States

Canada

U_____ S_____

M_____

Costa Rica

Pa_____

Pe_____

C_____

Colombia

Iceland *

Norway *

Liechtenstein *

Switzerland *

Israel

J_____

*   *member states of the European Free Trade Association*

B. **Complete the timeline and answer the questions with the help of the map in (A).**

Timeline of
Canada's FTAs

1989 —— with the U.S.
(Canada-U.S. Free
Trade Agreement*)

1994 —— with the U.S. and
Mexico
(North American Free
Trade Agreement)

1997 —┬— with I_____

       └— with Chile

2002 —— with Costa Rica

2009 —┬— with the European
Free Trade Association

       └— with Pe_____

2011 —— with Co_____

2012 —— with J_____

2013 —— with Pa_____

* *This FTA was superseded by the North American Free Trade Agreement in 1994.*

1.

Which was the first FTA between Canada and another country?

_____

2. Which FTA covers the largest free trade region in the world?

_____

3. Why do you think Canada signed the FTA in question 2 with the countries involved?

_____

_____

_____

4. What do you notice about the locations of Canada's trading partners?

_____

_____

_____

14

Canada and the United Nations

Canada, as one of the founding nations of the United Nations (UN), has been involved in many UN-related issues, including its efforts in achieving the Millennium Development Goals.

A. Fill in the blanks to complete the paragraphs about the UN and its Millennium Development Goals.

United Nations

| poverty | objectives | mortality | human rights |
| equality | cooperation | peace | education | maternal |

The United Nations, with 193 member states, is an international organization that was founded in 1945 with the purpose of maintaining international

1._____ and security, achieving international 2._____ in solving international problems, and promoting respect for 3._____ .

In September 2000, the United Nations Millennium Declaration was adopted with eight key 4._____ , called the Millennium Development Goals (MDGs), to be reached by 2015.

MDGs

 1 eradicating extreme _____ and hunger

 2 achieving universal primary _____

 3 promoting gender _____ and empowering women

 4 reducing child _____

 5 improving _____ health

 6 combating HIV/AIDS, malaria, and other diseases

 7 ensuring environmental sustainability

8 developing a global partnership for development

B. **Look at Canada's contributions and identify the MDGs they address. Draw the icons. Then answer the question.**

Canada's Efforts in Achieving the MDGs

Canada's Contributions	MDGs
helps improve access to maternal health care to reduce maternal and newborn deaths through its Children and Youth Strategy for developing countries	⬜ ⬜
supports local organizations in Haiti that protect and defend women's and girls' human rights	⬜
has provided $36 million to the African Development Bank so that people in rural areas of Africa have access to clean drinking water and the local governments can manage their water services more effectively	⬜
contributed $1.1 billion to sustainable economic growth in developing countries in 2012 – 2013 and helps sustainable agricultural development in developing countries through its Food Security Strategy	⬜
helps increase access to vaccines, immunization, and treatments (including malaria and HIV/AIDS) in developing countries to reduce child deaths	⬜ ⬜
contributed $165 million to basic education in Africa in 2011	⬜
works with other developing and developed countries, international organizations, and non-governmental organizations for the betterment of developing countries	⬜

Do some research and find one more way in which Canada has helped to achieve the UN's MDGs. Draw the icon.

_____

_____   ⬜

15

Children's Rights

The UN works to make the world a better place to live for everyone, including children. It adopted the Convention on the Rights of the Child in 1989, with Canada playing a key role in the negotiations that led to the adoption.

A. **Fill in the blanks to describe some of the children's rights in the UN's Convention on the Rights of the Child.**

All children have the right to:

play   harm
medical   culture
parents   opinion
education   name
government

- life.

- a 1._____ and a nationality.

- live with and be raised by their
  2._____ .

- be protected from 3._____ , abuse, and exploitation.

- voice their 4._____ .

- special care if they have special needs.

- have their basic needs fulfilled, such as food, clothes, shelter, and
  health and 5._____ care.

- receive help from the 6._____ if they are in need.

- good quality 7._____ .

- celebrate their 8._____ , speak their language, and practise their religion.

- 9._____ and rest.

- be protected from work that harms them.

The Convention defines a child as a person under 18 years old.

B. Read the paragraphs. Then answer the questions.

The Canadian Charter of Rights and Freedoms applies to all Canadian citizens, including children. However, it is only in reference to a child's right to receive an education in English or French where children are specifically mentioned.

Canada has ratified the Convention on the Rights of the Child, which means Canada is obliged to review and make changes to any laws and practices regarding children to ensure that the standards set by the Convention are reached. The implementation of the various aspects of the Convention is split between the federal government and the provinces. For example, on the federal level, more criminal laws are designed to prevent child abuse and the maximum punishments for those who violate the laws have been greatly increased. On the provincial level, there are universal health insurance plans that cover all children. Also, each province has its own laws and restrictions on child labour. For example, in Ontario, the minimum age for employment is 14. There are also laws that restrict the employment of children under 15 in logging operations and those under 16 in factories, in mines, and on construction sites.

1. Is the Convention on the Rights of the Child reflected in the Canadian Charter of Rights and Freedoms?

   _____

2. What changes in criminal laws show the implementation of the Convention?

   _____

   _____

3. What does Ontario do to protect the rights of children?

   _____

   _____

The World Health Organization

The World Health Organization (WHO) is the largest specialized agency of the UN. Apart from providing funds for WHO, Canada works closely with the agency to reduce global diseases.

A.   Check the roles of WHO in public health.

The Roles of WHO in Public Health

WHO was established in 1948, with the goal of achieving the highest possible level of health for everyone around the world.

A. leads countries in solving critical global health issues and works closely with different governments in cases that call for joint action

B. sets a health research agenda and makes sure valuable knowledge is distributed to all

C. provides funds for all health research and for medical supports in global health matters

D. sets and promotes norms and standards and makes sure that they are followed

E. states clearly the options for ethical and evidence-based policies

F. monitors global health situation and assesses health trends

G. provides technical support, encourages positive change, and builds sustainable institutional capacity

H. runs clinics and hospitals in countries where particular critical diseases are prevalent

B. **Read the paragraphs and the circle graph. Answer the questions.**

Canada works closely with WHO in reducing global diseases such as polio, malaria, HIV/AIDS, and tuberculosis.

Tuberculosis (TB) is a global health problem. While it is preventable and treatable, it still causes many deaths worldwide each year. Although the TB-related death rate is low in Canada, with 1607 reported TB cases in 2011, there are certain groups in the Canadian population that are more susceptible to the disease. It is important for Canada to play a role in the eradication of TB on the global front.

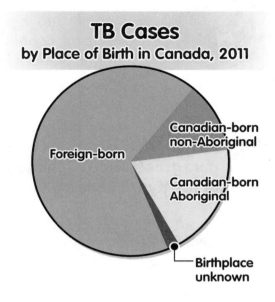

TB Cases
by Place of Birth in Canada, 2011

Canadian-born non-Aboriginal

Foreign-born

Canadian-born Aboriginal

Birthplace unknown

1. Why do you think Canada participates in WHO?

   _____

   _____

2. What does the circle graph show about the TB cases in Canada?

   _____

3. How does Canada benefit from its participation in WHO with regard to its TB issue?

   _____

   _____

4. Do you think Canada should continue to be a member of WHO? Why?

   _____

   _____

The Kyoto Protocol

Canada has a long history of leading international actions toward reducing air pollution and greenhouse gases. Canada participates in the United Nations Framework Convention on Climate Change (UNFCCC) and took an active role in the negotiation that led to the Kyoto Protocol.

A. Fill in the blanks to complete the paragraph about Canada's participation in the Kyoto Protocol.

1998   2005   6%   international
legally   carbon dioxide
reducing   climate   Japan

The Kyoto Protocol is an 1._____ agreement under the UNFCCC. It was adopted in Kyoto, 2._____ in 1997 and entered into force in 3._____ . It has the participation of 38 industrialized countries, including Canada, who have undertaken a 4._____ binding commitment to reducing six greenhouse gases: 5._____ , methane, nitrous oxide, sulphur hexafluoride, hydrofluorocarbons, and perfluorocarbons. Canada signed the agreement in 6._____ and ratified it in 2002, with the target of cutting greenhouse gas emissions to 7._____ below its 1990 level over the period of 2008 – 2012. However, in 2012, Canada withdrew its participation from the Kyoto Protocol, failing to meet the target. Nevertheless, Canada continues to support international efforts in combating global 8._____ change. Under the Copenhagen Accord, Canada has committed to 9._____ greenhouse gas emissions by 17% below its 2005 level by 2020.

B. Look at (A) again and the graph below. Answer the questions.

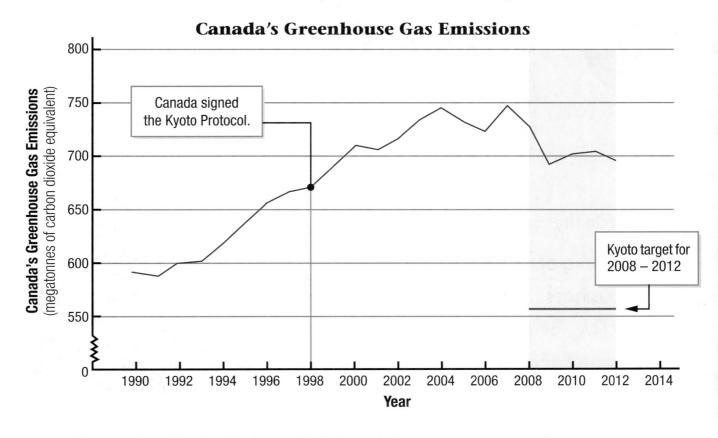

Canada's Greenhouse Gas Emissions

1. What is the Kyoto Protocol? What is its main purpose?

_____

_____

2. What does the graph show about Canada's greenhouse gas emissions since 1990 with regard to the Kyoto target?

_____

_____

3. Apart from undertaking the Kyoto Protocol, what has Canada done to show its effort in resolving global climate change issues?

_____

_____

Non-governmental Organizations

There are millions of non-governmental organizations (NGOs) around the world that focus on activities related to a wide variety of regional and global issues. Canadians volunteer and are involved in addressing various issues through different NGOs. Among them is Médecins Sans Frontières.

A. Circle the correct words.

A non-governmental organization (NGO) is a **business / non-profit** group that is formed by **citizens / politicians** who are passionate about a particular cause. The group can be local, national, or international. Most often, NGOs perform a variety of **military / humanitarian** activities, bringing about improvements in the quality of life for people.

One widely-known NGO is Médecins Sans Frontières (MSF), which is one of the world's leading **hunger / medical** relief organizations. Also known as Doctors Without Borders, MSF was established in 1971 by a small group of French **nurses / doctors** with the purpose of quickly responding to **public / personal** health emergencies around the world, without being intervened or stopped by political, economic, or religious reasons. As the winner of the 1999 Nobel **Peace / Physics** Prize, MSF is committed to independence, neutrality, and **injustice / impartiality** . Its mandate is to provide medical help for anyone who needs it in areas where there is no **medical / community** infrastructure.

B.   Fill in the blanks to complete the descriptions of MSF's actions.

food   improve   hygiene
managing   diseases   medical
officers   centres

MSF's Actions

1.   *Emergency healthcare:*

     providing immediate _____ aid when a catastrophe strikes

2.   *Mass vaccination campaigns:*

     immunizing people against rampant _____

3.   *Water and sanitation systems:*

     installing water points, water tanks, and hand pumps; distributing

     _____ kits

4.   *Therapeutic and supplementary nutrition:*

     setting up supplementary and therapeutic feeding _____

5.   *Distribution of drugs and supplies:*

     distributing medical supplies and relief supplies such as _____
     and plastic sheets

6.   *Training and health education:*

     helping medical _____ recognize medical emergencies;
     educating communities about specific viruses

7.   *Organization or rehabilitation of health facilities:*

     building and _____ new clinics and hospitals

8.   *Medical assistance within existing health facilities:*

     supporting and helping _____ existing clinics and health centres

C.   Research MSF Canada and answer the questions.

1.   MSF Canada formally joined the international movement in 19_____ .

2.   Three countries in which MSF Canada has managed health care projects:

_____

Free The Children

New NGOs have also been founded by Canadians. One such organization is Free The Children (now known as WE), which has become an international charity and youth movement and the world's largest network of children helping children through education.

A. Read the passage about Free The Children. Then fill in the information.

Free The Children was founded in 1995 by 12-year-old Canadian Craig Kielburger and 11 of his classmates. Its goals are to free children from poverty and exploitation and to free young people from the thought that they cannot do anything to bring positive changes to the world.

There are both domestic and international programs to achieve the goals. The domestic programs educate, engage, and empower youth in Canada, the United States, and the United Kingdom to be ambassadors for change and leaders in meaningful actions.

The international program, Adopt a Village, involves working with communities in eight countries in Africa, Asia, and Latin America to set a child-focused development approach that gives all members in the community education, skills, and opportunities to free themselves from poverty and build a healthy community. This is done by employing local staff in the sustainable development of five core pillars: education, clean water and sanitation, health, alternative income and livelihood, and agriculture and food security.

FREE THE CHILDREN

Founders: _____

_____

Year Founded: _____

Goals:

• _____

• _____

B. Draw lines to identify the impacts of Free The Children's programs.

Impacts of Free The Children's Programs

Domestic Programs

International Programs

- **A** $16 million worth of medical supplies have been delivered

- **B** approximately 30 000 women have become economically self-sufficient

- **C** participants have gained more confidence and are able to set goals and see them through to completion

- **D** most participants believe that they are responsible for addressing social justice issues

- **E** 68 801 student leaders engaged more than 517 000 students in social issues initiatives in 2012 – 2013

- **F** more than 650 schools and schoolrooms have been built

- **G** almost 80% of participants of voting age voted in the national election in 2011

- **H** more than one million people have access to clean water, health care, and sanitation

C. Explain the following quote from Free The Children in your own words.

> *Instead of making the world a better place for our children, we know we can make the world a better place with our children.*

_____

_____

_____

_____

_____

Canada's International Aid

Canada helps people living in poverty in developing countries by providing international aid to support initiatives that are sustainable and have positive impacts and results.

A. Fill in the blanks to complete the information about Canada's international aid.

> Canada has been distributing international aid to countries of focus.

Canada selects countries based on three criteria:

– 1._____

– ability to benefit meaningfully from Canada's aid

– alignment with Canada's 2._____ policy

Canada also focuses its support on three themes:

– increasing food security

  • food assistance and 3._____

  • sustainable 4._____ development

– securing the future of children and youth

  • access to quality basic 5._____

  • child survival including 6._____ , newborn, and child health

– stimulating sustainable economic growth

  • growing small and medium-sized 7._____

  • investing in people by increasing access to skill 8._____ and increasing learning opportunities

education
foreign
training
needs
agricultural
maternal
businesses
nutrition

B.   Read the map. Then complete the chart and answer the questions.

Top 10 Recipients of Canada's International Aid 2012 – 2013

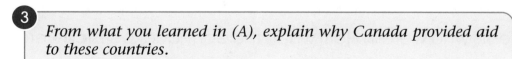

North America

Europe

Asia

Mali
~$119M

Afghanistan
~$131M

Haiti
~$139M

Bangladesh
~$127M

Côte d'Ivoire
~$148M

Africa

Ethiopia
~$181M

Ghana
~$141M

Tanzania
~$189M

Congo
~$157M

South America

Australia

Mozambique
~$105M

Top 10 Recipients

1 _____

2 _____

3 _____

4 _____

5 _____

6 _____

7 _____

8 _____

9 _____

10 _____

1. On which continent are most of the top 10 recipients of Canada's international aid in 2012 – 2013 located?

    _____

2. How many countries among the top 10 recipients are located on this continent?

    _____

3 *From what you learned in (A), explain why Canada provided aid to these countries.*

_____

_____

The 2010 Haiti Earthquake

When a devastating earthquake struck Haiti in 2010, Canada responded quickly in providing rescue and relief aid for the disaster-struck region. Many NGOs and Canadians also launched fundraising efforts to help the survivors of the earthquake.

A. Fill in the blanks to complete the description about the 2010 Haiti earthquake.

Earthquake damage in Jacmel

> communication   debt   donations
> humanitarian   security   aftershocks
> evacuated   infrastructure   earthquake

On January 12, 2010, an 1._____ measuring 7.0 on the Richter scale struck Haiti. With at least 52 2._____ measuring 4.5 or greater, this catastrophic earthquake claimed hundreds of thousands of lives, destroyed most parts of Haiti's capital city of Port-au-Prince, and severely damaged or destroyed vital 3._____, including hospitals and health care facilities, roads and transport facilities, electrical networks, and 4._____ systems, hampering rescue and relief efforts.

Canada responded to Haiti's appeals for 5._____ aid by deploying expert personnel from the Canadian Forces and the RCMP to help search and rescue, provide medical care and 6._____ services, and distribute food and water. 4620 Canadian citizens and permanent residents who were in Haiti when the earthquake struck were 7._____ on 49 flights. The federal government announced that it would match the 8._____ of Canadians, and committed to providing $550 million in aid and 9._____ relief to Haiti.

B. Sort the contributions into the correct groups. Write the letters.

Canadian Contributions in Response to the 2010 Haiti Earthquake

A Quebec pledged $3 million in emergency aid to Haiti.

B Over 137 000 families received emergency shelter supplies from the Canadian Red Cross.

C Ontario helped rebuild three schools destroyed in the earthquake in Haiti.

D Save the Children implemented an Emergency Education and Healthcare Project to address the needs of the people affected by the earthquake.

E Students in Toronto raised $630 000 for Haiti.

F Ontario provided medical supplies and equipment such as wheelchairs, stretchers, and surgical tables.

G The five Canadian charitable member agencies of the Humanitarian Coalition raised over $15.5 million for humanitarian response programs for the survivors.

H Canada for Haiti, a television special, raised $13.5 million to help those affected by the earthquake.

A 2013 survey found that almost 280 000 Haitians still lived in camps. Half of these camps had no health services and 15% of them had no basic protection services.

22

SARS in Canada

The outbreak of Severe Acute Respiratory Syndrome (SARS) in 2003 resulted in a global death toll of 774. Canada was the only country outside Asia that was significantly impacted by this highly infectious disease, with 44 deaths and about 25 000 Toronto residents quarantined.

A. **Fill in the blanks to complete the description of SARS in Canada.**

> hospitals   emergency   over
> provincial   Toronto   health
> respirators   precautions
> health care

Outbreak of SARS in Canada

2003

March and April

- The first outbreak of SARS in Canada occurred in 1._____ , Ontario in March and April 2003.

- A 2._____ emergency was declared on March 26. Province-wide directives on contact, droplet, and airborne 3._____ were instituted in hospitals and 4._____ units and strict measures were taken to contain the outbreak.

May

- In mid-May, the provincial emergency was lifted and many 5._____ workers, believing that the disease was under control, stopped wearing 6._____ and other protective equipment.

- Several days later, a new cluster of cases was reported and the second wave of SARS started. Strict controls were re-imposed, closing the 7._____ where new cases were found and limiting access to 8._____ rooms in all other hospitals in Toronto.

July

- In July 2003, SARS in Toronto was officially 9._____ .

B. **Read what the people say. Then answer the questions.**

I live in downtown Toronto. I learned about the outbreak of SARS from the news. I knew it was a highly infectious and fatal disease, but since there was little spread into the community, I thought it shouldn't be a problem living my life as usual. I dined out, met with my friends, and enjoyed recreational activities at my leisure. Everyone on the street looked normal and no one wore a mask.

One student at my school showed symptoms of SARS so the school was temporarily closed. Teachers and students were asked to go into voluntary quarantine. We had to stay home from school as a precaution. I stayed in my bedroom most of the time for a whole week and wore a mask whenever Mom brought me food, but I know that a few students from my school didn't heed the advice and snuck out.

1. Do you think Logan handled the outbreak well? Why?

   _____

   _____

2. If you were Logan, what would you have done?

   _____

   _____

3. Why is quarantine necessary during the outbreak of an infectious disease?

   _____

   _____

4. Why did Mia wear a mask when her mom brought her food?

   _____

   _____

23

Invasive Species in Canada

With the growth in international trade, travel, and transportation, the threats of invasive species have become a growing worldwide concern. Canada, with its extensive coastline and close proximity to the Great Lakes, is especially vulnerable to the threats of invasive species.

Decide whether the introduction of each invasive species was intentional or unintentional. Identify the species that brought about the impact and the measures taken to control them. Then answer the question.

Invasive species are the harmful non-native plant and animal species that threaten the environment, economy, society, and even people's health in an area. Some invasive species were introduced to Canada intentionally while others were unintentional. They cost Canadians billions of dollars annually in revenue loss and control measures. The three levels of government, NGOs, universities, industries, business groups, and the general public have to work together to resolve these issues.

 Zebra Mussel   (an _____ introduction)

came to North America in the late 1980s through ballast water discharged from cargo ships

 Emerald Ash Borer   (an _____ introduction)

believed to have been introduced first to the U.S. in May 2002 and then to Canada in July 2002 through untreated wood packaging material

 Common Buckthorn   (an _____ introduction)

introduced to North America in the 1880s as an ornamental shrub, and has since spread throughout eastern and central North America, including southern Ontario

Impact of Invasive Species

- has killed millions of ash trees in North America
- has led to the loss of valuable timber for furniture, building, and recreational products

Measure

- has rooted out native mussels from Lake Erie, Lake St. Clair, and the Detroit River, all of which border both Canada and the U.S.
- colonizes on a variety of surfaces rapidly, such as buoys and pipes, thereby sinking or clogging them

Measure

- forms dense thickets under which few native plant species can grow, thereby reducing biodiversity
- alters nitrogen levels in the soil in favour of its growth, which in turn discourages the growth of native species

Measure

Control Measures

A educating the public on identifying and removing the invasive species

B making laws to ensure that ships entering Canadian waters manage their ballast water in a responsible manner

C banning the transportation of firewood to certain places

From what you have learned in this unit, why do you think the resolution of the issue of invasive species requires international cooperation and collaboration?

_____

_____

Canada's Tourist Sources and Destinations

Millions of Canadians visit other countries and millions of tourists travel to Canada each year. There are different factors that affect people's choices of destination.

A. Look at the map. With the help of the coordinates, name the top six countries visited by Canadians. Then write the coordinates of the top six countries where tourists came from.

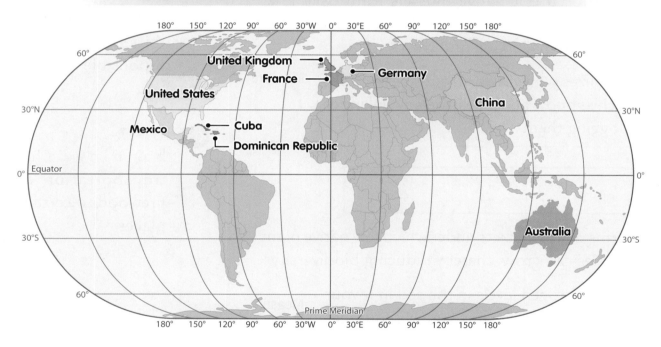

Canada's Tourist Sources and Destinations (2012)

Coordinates are used to locate places on a map.

Coordinates

latitude	**longitude**
horizontal lines	vertical lines

Cuba is located 22° north of the equator and 80° west of the prime meridian.

e.g. Cuba
Coordinates:

22° N   80° W

Top 6 countries visited by Canadians (2012)

	Country	Coordinates
1.	_____	39° N 112° W
2.	_____	27° N 110° W
3.	_____	22° N 79° W
4.	_____	53° N 1° W
5.	_____	18° N 69° W
6.	_____	49° N 2° E

Top 6 countries tourists to Canada came from (2012)

	Country	Coordinates
1.	United States	_____
2.	United Kingdom	_____
3.	France	_____
4.	Germany	_____
5.	China	_____
6.	Australia	_____

B. Answer the questions.

Factors Affecting Tourists' Destination Choices

 budget   location   travel time   language   means of transport    family and friend reunions

1. Why do you think the United States was the top tourist source and destination in 2012?

_____

_____

2. Apart from the United States, which countries are on both lists?

_____

3. Why do you think these countries are on both lists?

_____

_____

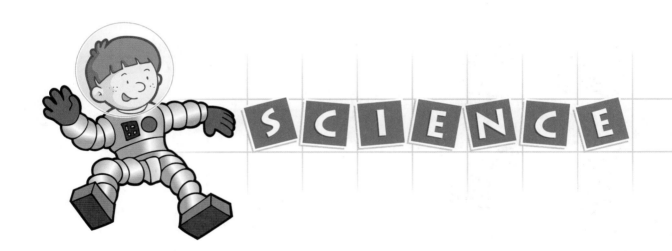

Classification of Living Things (1)

- We classify things into groups in order to make things easier to understand.
- All living things share a set of characteristics in order to survive.
- All living things are grouped into the first level of classification known as a "kingdom". There are five kingdoms.

A. Sort the things into groups. Write the letters.

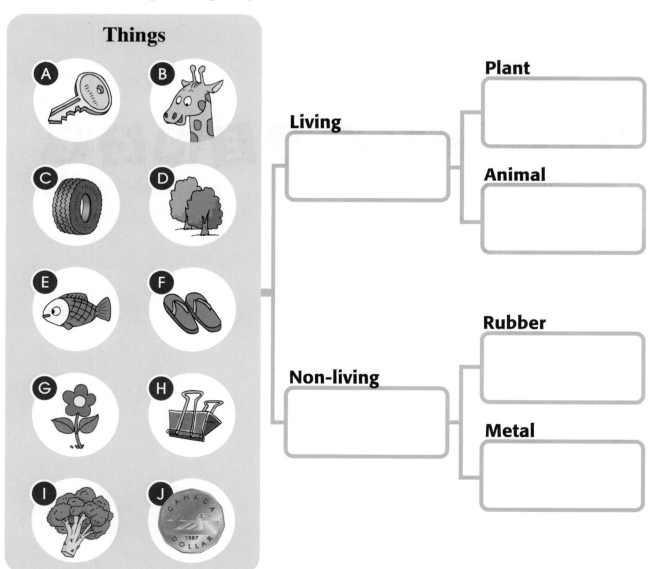

B. Check the sentence parts that make true statements about living things and put a cross for the false ones.

All living things...

(A) can fly.

(B) must adapt to the environment.

(C) can make tools.

(D) are made up of cells.

(E) can show movement.

(F) must get and use energy.

(G) must reproduce.

(H) can grow and develop.

C. Name the five kingdoms.

animals   fungi   plants   protists   monera

═══ **Five Kingdoms of Living Things** ═══

1.

bacteria

_____

2.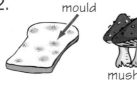

mould

mushrooms

_____

3.

_____

4.

_____

5.

microscopic organisms

_____

Science Fact

Carolus Linnaeus (1707–1778) is known as the "Father of Taxonomy". The classification system that he developed is still in use today and is based on the structures of organisms.

Carolus Linnaeus

Classification of Living Things (2)

- Scientists use a seven-level classification system to organize all living things into groups. The names of the groups are in Latin.
- Organisms with similar body structures are placed in the same group.

Name: Eric Spencer
Scientific Name: Homo sapiens
Class: Mammalia

A. **Fill in the missing letters to complete the seven levels of classification. Then use the chart to answer the questions.**

class   family   genus   kingdom   order   phylum   species

1.

Levels of Classification \ Organisms	Human	Housefly	Grey Wolf	Chimpanzee
K	Animalia	Animalia	Animalia	Animalia
P	Chordata	Arthropoda	Chordata	Chordata
C	Mammalia	Insecta	Mammalia	Mammalia
O	Primates	Diptera	Carnivora	Primates
F	Hominidae	Muscidae	Canidae	Hominidae
G	Homo	Musca	Canis	Pan
S	sapiens	domestica	lupus	troglodytes

2. At what level are all the organisms in the same group?

_____

3. At what levels are we in the same group as the chimpanzee?

_____

B. **Read what Eric says and look at the chart on the previous page. Write the scientific names for the other organisms in the chart.**

> The genus and species names are used to give an organism its scientific name. Our scientific name is **Homo sapiens**.

Scientific Name

1. Housefly _____

2. Grey Wolf _____

3. Chimpanzee _____

C. **In each group, one organism does not belong because of its body structure. Cross out the one that does not belong. Then write a reason below it.**

- no backbone
- cannot make food
- not in the cat family

Science Fact

Scientists have identified and described about 1.75 million different species to date, but there are many more. New ones are being discovered every day.

Invertebrates

You have plenty of bones now!

- Invertebrates are animals that do not have a backbone.

A. Colour the invertebrates in the picture.

B. Look at the phylum names of the major groups of invertebrates. Find the common examples of the groups. Then match the groups with the descriptions. Write the letters.

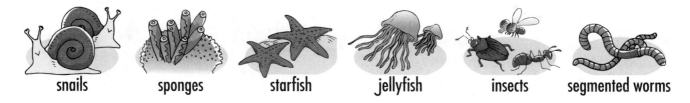

snails   sponges   starfish   jellyfish   insects   segmented worms

Groups of Invertebrates
Phylum name (common example)

Porifera

(sp_____) ◯

Coelenterata

(j_____) ◯

Arthropoda

(i_____) ◯

Mollusca

(sn_____) ◯

Echinodermata

(st_____) ◯

Annelida

(s_____ w_____) ◯

A This organism feeds by filtering captured food as water flows through its body.

B Some members of this group have segmented bodies that contain five "hearts".

C This spiny-skinned animal has a water tube system that allows it to move and hunt for food.

D This animal has stinging cells that are used to paralyze its prey.

E These animals have a hard, jointed "exoskeleton" that protects and supports the body.

F Most of these animals have shells.

Science Fact

Invertebrates make up about 95% of all animals and most of them live in the ocean.

Arthropods

- Arthropods are the most diverse of all the invertebrates.
- Like all other life forms, arthropods have adapted to life on Earth in many different ways.

A. Read what the arthropods say. Match the sentences with the characteristics of arthropods. Write the letters.

1.

Other members of my class have mouthparts different from mine. It all depends on what you eat!

_____

Characteristics of Arthropods

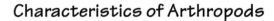

A compound eyes

B adapted mouthparts

C exoskeleton

D segmented body

E jointed appendages

2.

I don't mean to brag, but I have many, many more sections than all of you guys put together!

_____

3.

If I could sell kneepads to football-playing millipedes, I'd be rich!

_____

4.

I can see almost all around me, so don't try to sneak up on me!

_____

5.

When I was really young and growing a lot, I would go and hide somewhere and shed my covering once a day. Now that I'm older, these moults are less frequent.

_____

B. **Fill in the blanks with the given words to show the different groups of arthropods.**

Phylum Arthropoda

Myriapoda
Arachnida
Crustacea
Insecta
many
3
0
4
1

Class: C_____

- 5 or more pairs of legs
- 2 pairs of antennae

Class: I_____

- _____ pairs of legs
- 1 pair of antennae

Class: A_____

- _____ pair(s) of legs
- _____ pair(s) of antennae

Class: M_____

- _____ pair(s) of legs
- _____ pair(s) of antennae

C. **Fill in the blanks with the given words.**

1. The body of an insect is divided into three segments: head, _____ , and abdomen.

   wings
   thorax
   exoskeleton

2. Insects are the only invertebrates that can fly, and most insects have two pairs of _____ .

3. Insects have a tough, jointed _____ that protects their many organ systems.

Science Fact

Cockroaches, when running at full speed, actually raise themselves up onto their two hind legs! Creepy.

Vertebrates

- Vertebrates have a set of very specific characteristics.
- There are five groups of vertebrates.

A. Write "true" or "false" for each sentence.

1. Most vertebrates reproduce sexually, either by laying eggs or giving birth to live young.

   _____

2. All vertebrates live on land.   _____

3. Most vertebrates have jaws.   _____

4. Some vertebrates lack a braincase.   _____

5. Vertebrates do not display bilateral symmetry, which means the left- and right-hand sides of the body are equal.   _____

6. The skeleton of a vertebrate grows with the animal and does not have to be shed like the external skeleton of an arthropod.

   _____

7. All vertebrates have an internal skeleton that is usually made of bones.

   _____

B. **Name the five groups of vertebrates. Then cross out the one that does not belong in each group.**

1. F_____

2. A_____

3. M_____

4. B_____

5. R_____

C. **Fill in the blanks.**

1. **fish/mammal**

    a. Scales are to _____ as hair is to _____ .

    b. Laying eggs is to _____ as giving birth to live young is to _____ .

    c. Lungs are to _____ as gills are to _____ .

2. **bird/reptile/amphibian**

    a. Dry skin is to _____ as moist skin is to _____ .

    b. Feathers are to _____ as scales are to _____ .

Science Fact

An adult amphibian's skin must be kept moist because it is an organ that aids its "breathing".

Vertebrate Adaptations

- *Vertebrates have body structures and behaviours that are adaptations to their environments.*

A. Match the subject being discussed in the newspaper with each topic. Write the letter.

A ...have many variations that are adapted to obtaining the food that they need to survive.

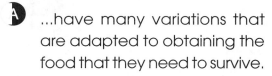

B ...are hollow which make them very light.

C ...are used to nourish their young with the milk that they produce.

D ...have a leathery covering that makes it possible for them to be laid on land where it is safer than if they were laid in water.

E ...molars, canines, and incisors that allow for their food to be torn into smaller pieces and chewed.

F ...have gills when they are young, but use these structures when they are older.

○ reptile eggs

○ amphibian lungs

○ bird beaks

○ mammary glands

○ bird bones

○ the teeth of mammals

B. **Read what Leo says. Fill in the blanks.**

The prefix "endo" comes from the Greek word that means "within", whereas "exo" means "outside". "Thermic" means "heat".

warm	constant	exothermic	cold
insulator	endothermic	overheating	

1. Birds and mammals are _____ , or warm-blooded, which means that they can maintain a _____ body temperature through adaptations found within the body.

2. Reptiles are _____ , or cold-blooded, and must find shady or cool places during the heat of the day to avoid _____ .

3. Shivering is something that a _____ -blooded animal does to try to raise its body temperature when it gets too _____ .

4. Mammals have bodies covered in hair to act as an _____ against the cold.

Science Fact

Humans used to think that one of the things that "elevated" us above all other animals was our ability to make and use tools. We now know that many species of birds and other primates such as chimpanzees share with us this incredible skill.

7

Air

- Though we cannot see it, air is matter. It takes up space, it has weight, and it expands when heated.

There's air inside!

A. **Fill in the blanks with the given words. Then colour the heavier object in each pair of pictures to tell which one has more air.**

Anything with mass is pulled toward the Earth by the force of gravity. Your weight depends on your mass and the gravity pulling you down. If air has

1._____ , 2._____ is also pulling it down,

so it must also have 3._____ .

weight
gravity
mass

4. The heavier one is...

a.

b.

B. **Match each property of air with its example.**

Properties of Air

1. has weight •

2. takes up space •

3. expands when heated •

• Your lungs are filled with air when you breathe in.

• Warm air rises because it is lighter than cool air.

• A deflated basketball weighs less than an inflated basketball.

Experiment – Newspapers

Things needed:

- a ruler
- newspaper
- a table

Because air has weight, it presses on things. This is called air pressure. We do this experiment to find out how much air presses on a newspaper and see if there is enough weight to keep the ruler from flying off the table.

Steps:

1. Put a ruler on a table so it is slightly hanging over the edge.

2. Layer two open sheets of newspaper on the table, covering the part of the ruler that's on the table.

3. With a quick movement, hit the ruler with the side of your hand.

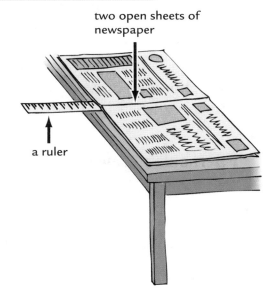

two open sheets of newspaper

a ruler

The paper itself does not have enough weight to prevent the ruler from moving. What is providing the extra weight?

_____

_____

Science Fact

The higher you are up in the sky, the less air there is pressing down on you. That is why air pressure is higher at sea level than at the top of a mountain.

air pressure

less air — low

more air — high

8

Bernoulli's Principle

- Bernoulli's Principle states that the faster air moves, the lower its pressure.
- A shape that causes air pressure to be higher on one side than it is on another is called an airfoil.
- Streamlining helps an object move through air by giving it less air resistance.

faster moving air, lower pressure

Faster, Teddy!

A. **Write the correct word to complete Bernoulli's Principle. Then label the diagram with "higher" or "lower".**

Bernoulli's Principle

Because air has weight, it exerts pressure. A scientist, Daniel Bernoulli, discovered that moving air exerts

1. _____ pressure than still air.
   more/less

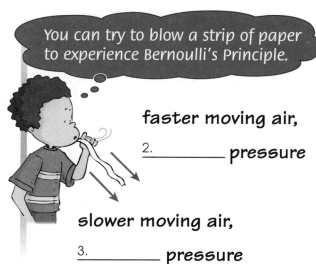

You can try to blow a strip of paper to experience Bernoulli's Principle.

faster moving air,

2. _____ pressure

slower moving air,

3. _____ pressure

B. **Look at the diagram. Fill in the blanks to complete the paragraph with the words in bold.**

An Airfoil

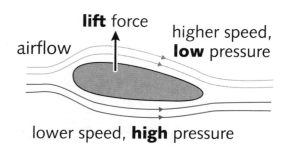

lift force

airflow

higher speed, **low** pressure

lower speed, **high** pressure

When an airfoil moves through air, air whooshes over it at a higher speed than the air below. Above the airfoil, air pressure is 1. _____ . 2. _____ air pressure underneath will 3. _____ the airfoil into the air.

C.   Circle the things that have an airfoil.

D.   Redesign the objects to make them streamlined.

bike helmet

toy car

Things designed to move through air easily are aerodynamic or streamlined.

Science Fact

Bernoulli's Principle was first used to describe movement through water. It was later found to be true for movement through all fluids, including air.

Flight (1)

- Four forces act on anything that flies – lift, gravity, drag, and thrust.

A.   Tell the forces at work in the diagram and for the sentences.

1.

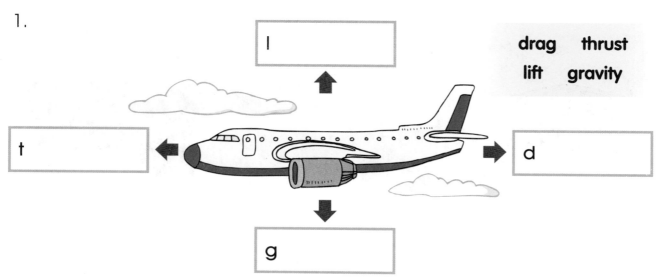

| l |
| t |
| d |
| g |

drag   thrust
lift   gravity

2.   A parachute gives enough air resistance to slow a parachutist's fall to the ground.

_____

3.   Lower air pressure above a wing means the high pressure below pushes the wing upward.

_____

4.   Propellers work by propelling an airplane forward.

_____

5.

This is the force overcome by lift, and will bring all things that fly back to the ground when lift is absent.

_____

B. **What else provides the force that allows each of these to fly?   What force is provided?   Unscramble the words to find the answers.**

1.

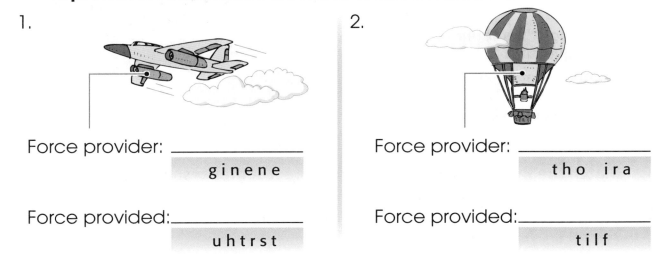

Force provider: _____

g i n e n e

Force provided:_____

u h t r s t

2.

Force provider: _____

t h o   i r a

Force provided:_____

t i l f

C. **Complete the crossword puzzle with the help of the given words.**

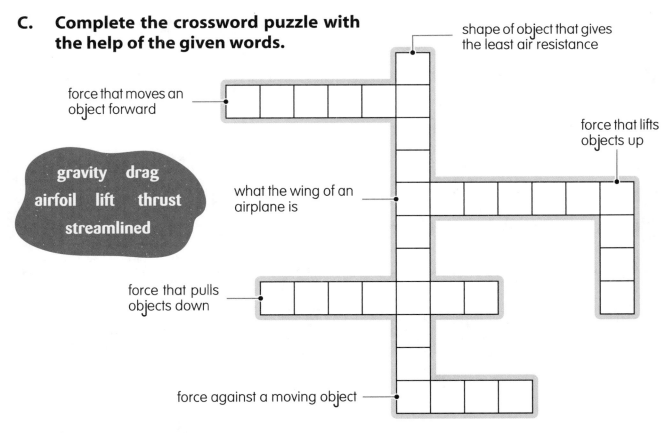

shape of object that gives the least air resistance

force that moves an object forward

gravity   drag
airfoil   lift   thrust
streamlined

what the wing of an airplane is

force that lifts objects up

force that pulls objects down

force against a moving object

The flying squirrel glides from tree to tree. It does not have the thrust to go further than that.

10

Flight (2)

- *Humans have made many different machines capable of flight.*
- *The shapes of our flying machines are similar to things found in nature, such as birds, fish, and the seeds of some plants.*

A.   Match the flying machines with the correct sentences.   Write the letters.

A   For this machine's flight, it relies on the principle that hot air expands and is lighter than cooler air.

B   This paper toy is streamlined and propelled by the human hand.

C   Though it does not have wings, the curve of this toy is enough of an airfoil to make it fly in the wind.

D   This powerful engine uses an enormous amount of fuel for its strong thrust.

E   Air resistance allows this to carry its load slowly to the ground.

F   With no engine of its own, this aircraft is towed into the air.

G   The rotor blades above this aircraft are airfoils.

H   An engine propels this winged aircraft.

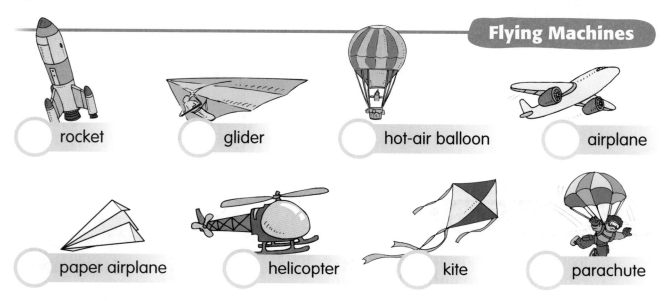

Flying Machines

rocket   glider   hot-air balloon   airplane

paper airplane   helicopter   kite   parachute

B. **What do flying machines have in common with things found in nature? Find their similarities. Write their names on the lines.**

1. They float in the air due to air resistance, or drag.

   _____ and _____

2. Lift comes from airfoil-shaped blades that rotate round and round.

   _____ and _____

3. They are streamlined for moving easily through fluid, and get their lift from airfoils at their sides.

   _____ and _____

C. **List six things that can fly.**

_____   _____

_____   _____

_____   _____

Science Fact

There is no air on the moon, so there is no air resistance. Parachutes and anything else that needs air resistance to fly cannot be used on the moon.

11

History of Air and Space Travel

- *Inventors from all over the world and through many ages are a part of the history of flight.*

A. Check the correct picture to match each event.

1. The Montgolfier brothers flew their hot-air balloon in front of a cheering crowd in France. A few months later, they sent up some farm animals before the first ride with human passengers.

A

B

1783 in France   1783 in Italy

2. Yuri Gagarin was the first human in space! The Russian man orbited the Earth once before coming home.

A   B

Yuri Gagarin in 1961   Yuri Gagarin Memorial in 1980

3. Otto Lilienthal jumped off a hill strapped to his glider and flew – it worked! He looked like a bird in the sky.

A   B

1791 in France   1891 in Germany

4. Wilbur and Orville Wright flew the first powered, heavier-than-air flying machine – the first airplane!

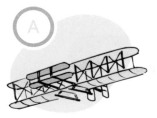 

A   B

1903 in the U.S.   1903 in the U.S.

B. Complete the timeline to show the important flight events. Locate the years and write the events.

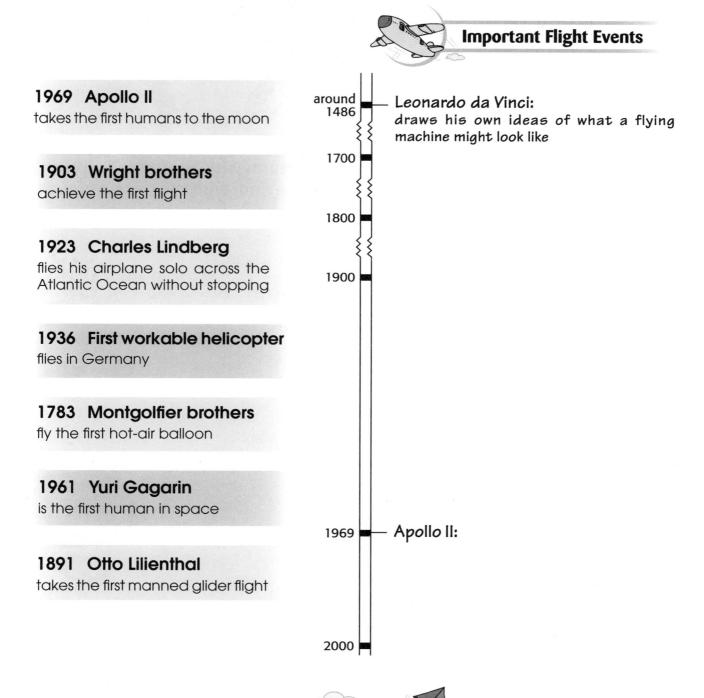

Important Flight Events

1969 Apollo II
takes the first humans to the moon

1903 Wright brothers
achieve the first flight

1923 Charles Lindberg
flies his airplane solo across the Atlantic Ocean without stopping

1936 First workable helicopter
flies in Germany

1783 Montgolfier brothers
fly the first hot-air balloon

1961 Yuri Gagarin
is the first human in space

1891 Otto Lilienthal
takes the first manned glider flight

around 1486 — Leonardo da Vinci: draws his own ideas of what a flying machine might look like

1700

1800

1900

1969 — Apollo II:

2000

 Science Fact

Inventors of other flying machines studied kites, believed to be invented in China more than 2500 years ago.

12

Static and Current Electricity

Hi, Judy. You have a new hairstyle today.

- Electric energy is in one of two forms: static electricity or current electricity.

A. **Fill in the blanks and label each group of pictures with "static" or "current". Then draw lines to match the pictures on the right with the correct groups.**

1. _____ electricity is the electrical charge produced when two things rub together.

2. _____ electricity is very useful to us. It can be transformed into light, heat, or motion energy.

_____ electricity

Examples:

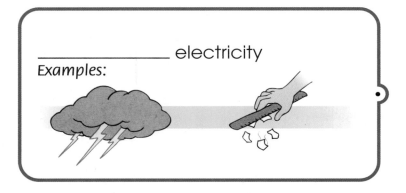

_____ electricity

Examples:

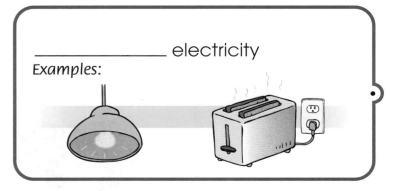

B. **Fill in the blanks with the given words. Then draw arrows to show the path of the electrical current in each picture.**

1.

positive terminal

electrical current

negative terminal

negative   electrons   positive

Electrical currents are made from _____ flowing through wires. The electrical current flows from the _____ terminal of the battery to the _____ terminal.

2. a. 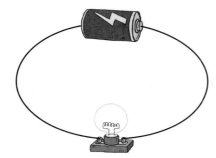   b.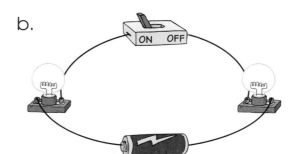

Experiment – Static electricity

Things needed:
- *a balloon*
- *a wool sweater*

Steps:

1. Rub a balloon vigorously on the wool sweater.

2. Hold the balloon up to a wall and let go.

3. Static electricity will hold the balloon to the wall if the room is dry enough.

On a dry day, the same balloon can be used to raise the hair on your head, or bend a slow stream of water coming out of a tap.

Science Fact

It is common to feel the static electricity when you touch something after dragging stocking feet on a carpet. Did you know you can also see static electricity if the room is dark?

13

Circuits

- We use symbols to draw an electrical circuit. The drawing is called a schematic.
- An electrical circuit is the path of current electricity.

A. Name the objects represented by the symbols.

wire   switch   light bulb   battery

1. _____

2. _____

3. _____

4. _____

B. Match the circuit with the correct schematic. Write the letters.

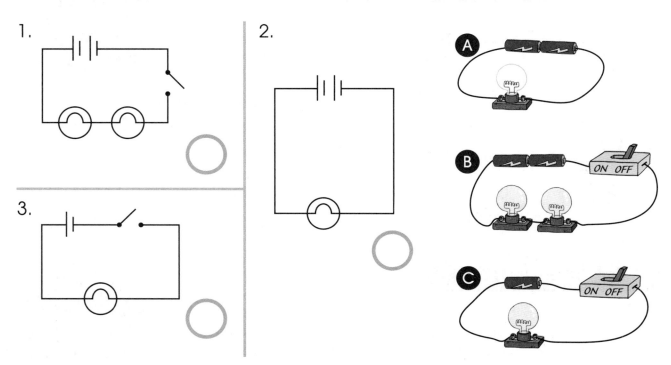

1.

2.

3.

A

B

C

C. Complete or draw the schematics of the circuits.

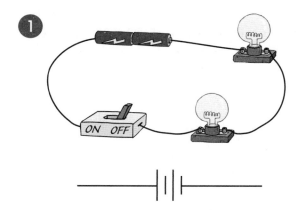

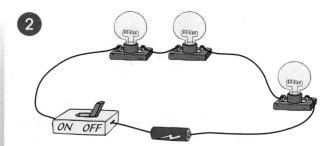

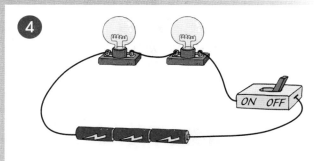

Science Fact

How fast does electricity move through a circuit?
As fast as the speed of light.

14

Conductors and Insulators

- A closed circuit is one in which electricity flows uninterrupted, while a circuit with a disrupted connection is an open circuit.
- A material that allows electricity to move easily through it is called a conductor.
- An insulator is a material that resists electricity moving through it.

A. Colour the light bulb yellow if the circuit is closed.

1.

2.

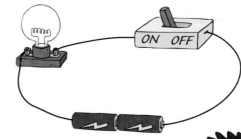

3.

4.

5.

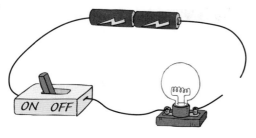

6.

B. Circle the objects that conduct electricity to make a closed circuit.

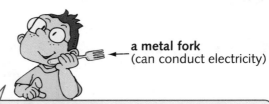

a metal fork
(can conduct electricity)

Metal generally conducts electricity well, while plastic and rubber resist electricity.

1.

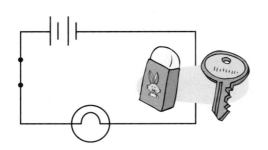

2.

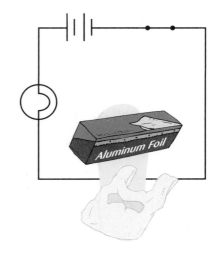

3.

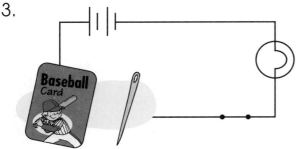

C. Fill in the blanks.

1. The plastic coating around electrical wires acts as _____ .
   a conductor/an insulator

2. The metal filament inside a light bulb _____ electrical currents.
   conducts/insulates

3. Standing in a puddle of water while operating an electrical appliance could cause an electric shock because water can be an electrical

   _____ .
   conductor/insulator

4. The wire in a circuit acts as _____ .
   a conductor/an insulator

Science Fact

Electricity can injure and even kill when handled improperly. Electrical technicians wear thick rubber gloves, which are electrical insulators, as a precaution against electric shock.

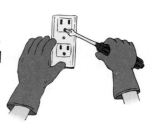

15

Electricity

- There are two types of electrical circuits – series and parallel.
- Electrical infrastructures are in place to bring electricity from the power source to our homes and businesses.

A. **Fill in the blanks and identify the type of electrical circuit in each diagram. Write "series" or "parallel" on the lines.**

1.

_____ circuits are connected in a chain-like order. What happens in one part of the chain affects every other part. _____ circuits have individually connected devices. If one light bulb goes out in a parallel circuit, the circuit isn't broken.

2.

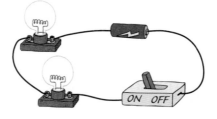

_____ circuit

3.

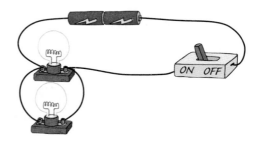

_____ circuit

4.

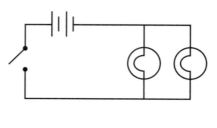

_____ circuit

5.

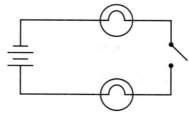

_____ circuit

B. **Draw lines to complete the circuits.**

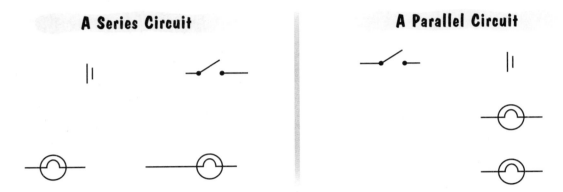

A Series Circuit

A Parallel Circuit

C. **Label the pictures by writing the letters. Then draw a line to show the path that electricity takes from its source to our homes.**

A home   **B** electrical outlet   **C** high-voltage power lines

D substation   **E** hydroelectric dam   **F** low-voltage power lines

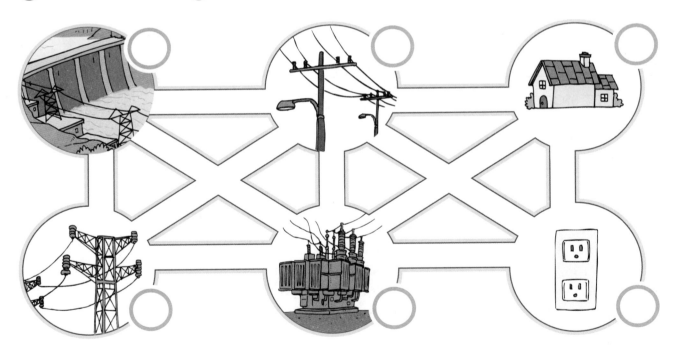

Science Fact

Thomas Edison (1847–1931) was the inventor who brought electric lights into our homes. Before he invented the light bulb in 1879, inefficient gas lamps lit up streets and homes.

Birth Certificate

1879

16

Sources of Electricity

- Electrical energy can come from many different sources.
- Electric meters outside of homes and businesses measure the amount of electricity we use.

A. Fill in the blanks with the given words to complete the sentences about electrical energy sources.

Electrical Energy Sources

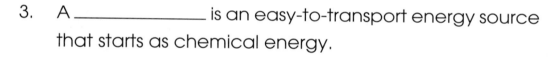

oil   wind   gas   solar
coal   tides   battery
geothermal   nuclear
moving water

1. A renewable energy source captured by turbines in the air is _____ .

2. The daily rhythm of _____ can be a reliable and renewable source of energy in coastal areas.

3. A _____ is an easy-to-transport energy source that starts as chemical energy.

4. _____ energy produces electricity from the heat of rocks beneath the ground.

5. Hydroelectric dams are what we use to harness _____ as an energy source.

6. _____ energy does not pollute the atmosphere, but we are unable to safely dispose of its waste.

7. Three non-renewable energy sources are _____ , _____ , and _____ . That means the supply will run out quicker than it can be replaced.

8. The energy source that makes use of the sun's rays is _____ energy.

B. Read what the technician says. Record and find the electricity consumption of each household in a given period. Then answer the questions.

These five small dials on an electric meter show readings. When the hand of a dial is between two numbers, we read the smaller number, except for 0 and 9. Electrical consumption can be found by finding the difference between previous and present readings.

reading: 46 502 kWh

kilowatt-hours

1.

previous reading:

_____ kWh

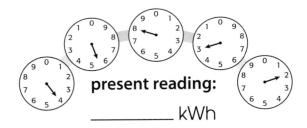

present reading:

_____ kWh

Amount of electricity used:

_____ kWh

2.

previous reading:

_____ kWh

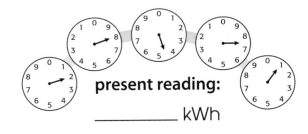

present reading:

_____ kWh

Amount of electricity used:

_____ kWh

3. Which household consumed more electricity? _____

Electricity is a secondary energy source. This means it needs something else, like coal or wind, to be produced.

17

Motion

- Motion can be classified as linear, rotational, reciprocating, or oscillating.
- When things that have mass are made to move, they gain something known as kinetic energy. It is the energy of things that are moving and can be used to do many interesting things.

I am oscillating.

A. **Name the motion shown in each picture. Then draw a line to match its definition.**

Linear

Oscillating

Rotational

Reciprocating

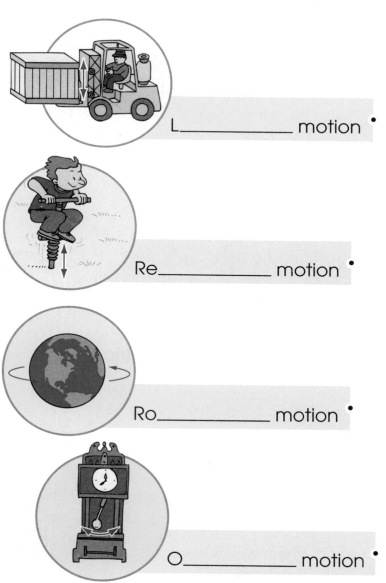

L_____ motion •

Re_____ motion •

Ro_____ motion •

O_____ motion •

• motion in a circle around an axis

• motion in a straight line

• straight back and forth motion

• an arching back and forth motion

B. There are various types of movements that give people the kinetic energy to do what they do. Name the type of movement displayed by each person by using the words given on the previous page.

1.

_____

2.

A _____

B _____

3.

_____

Try this.

Some machines can perform many different types of motion at the same time. Can you give me an example with 2 types of motion? Then act them out with your body.

_____

_____

Science Fact

The International Space Station (ISS) makes 15.72 orbits around the Earth every day, and as of November 20, 2014, has been in orbit for 5844 days.

18

Friction

A deeper tread design increases friction.

- Friction is the resistance to motion that is experienced when one moving surface comes in contact with another.
- There are things that can be done to increase or decrease friction.

A. Look at each picture and find what will happen when friction is not there. Check the correct answer.

1.

   Ⓐ The rock climber will still be firmly planted and look stable.

   Ⓑ The rock climber will be left hanging, as his hands and shoes will no longer grip the rock.

2.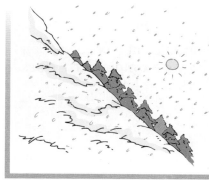

   Ⓐ Avalanche! The snow on the top of the mountain will slide to the bottom.

   Ⓑ The snow will keep stacking up and become more stable.

3.

   Ⓐ The ball will roll back to your team.

   Ⓑ The ball will roll forever!

B. **"The Friction News" is about to go to press.** **Complete the newspaper clippings with the given words.**

> oil   ball bearings   chalk

1. "...fans of in-line skating can rest easy knowing that their wheels will spin fast and not wear out. Inside the wheels, _____ have been used to _____ friction that occurs.

increase/decrease
The _____ sliding friction is replaced with the

greater/lesser
_____ rolling friction of the round metal balls..."

greater/lesser

2. "...the _____ is used by gymnasts to _____ the amount of friction between

increase/decrease
their hands and the mats, rings, and bars, giving them a better grip."

3. "...intense heat that happens inside a car's engine is the result of the metal surfaces rubbing against each other which _____ friction. This can be

increases/decreases
_____ by using _____,

increased/reduced
a very effective lubricant."

Science Fact

Some fish are covered in a slime that protects their bodies from chemicals in the water as well as from drying out. It is also thought that this substance helps reduce friction when the fish move through the water.

19

Movement and Levers

- The three classes of simple levers are designed to do different things with the force that is applied.
- Levers can be used together to form more complicated machines, which transmit motion and force.

A. **Look at the pictures showing the three classes of levers. Fill in the blanks with "effort", "load", or "fulcrum".**

1st Class Lever

The fulcrum is between the _____

and the _____ .

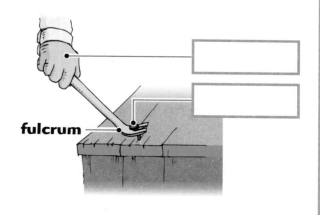

fulcrum

2nd Class Lever

The load is between the _____

and the _____ .

load

3rd Class Lever

The effort is between the _____

and the _____ .

fulcrum

B. **Look at the pictures on the previous page again. Circle the correct words to complete the sentences.**

1. The crowbar increases / decreases the effort force, thus making it easier to remove nails or pry materials apart.

2. The wheelbarrow distributes the weight of its load / effort force between the wheel and the load / effort force , thus making it easier to carry and move heavy things.

3. The fishing rod does not increase / increases effort force; in fact, the force is actually less / more . The advantage of using this tool is that it increases / decreases the distance between the fulcrum and the load force which is ideal for casting out the line.

C. **Two levers of the same class have been put together in each mechanism. Write which class of lever it is.**

1. A nutcracker has 2 _____ class levers put together to get the shells of nuts cracked open.

2. A pair of scissors is made up of 2 _____ class levers.

3. A pair of tweezers is made up of 2 _____ class levers.

Science Fact

A parrot's beak is a fine example of how nature has followed good physics. The parrot has a built-in nutcracker, enabling it to crack the shell of even the toughest nut.

20

Solar System

- The solar system is an orderly system. Each planet and asteroid has a place and a predictable path of movement.
- Telescopes allow us to learn more about distant objects in the solar system.

A.   Write "true" or "false" for each sentence.

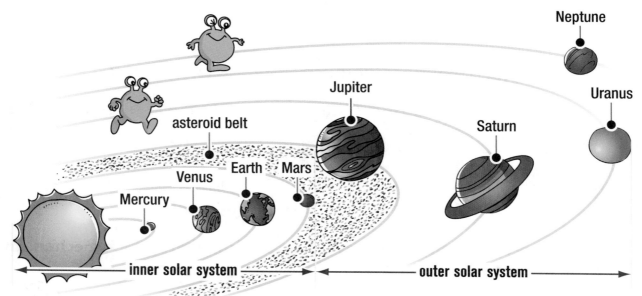

1.   Venus is the closest planet to the sun.   _____

2.   Jupiter is the largest planet in the solar system.   _____

3.   There are eight planets in the solar system.   _____

4.   The asteroid belt is between the inner and outer solar systems.   _____

5.   All the planets in the solar system revolve around the sun.   _____

6.   Earth's place in the solar system is between Jupiter and Mars.   _____

7.   The planets in the outer solar system are gaseous planets, so Mars is a gaseous planet.   _____

B. **Read what the boy says. Help him label each object in the solar system. Match each object with its descriptions. Write the letters.**

Objects in the night sky sometimes look different with the naked eye than they do through a telescope. Each object is described as it is seen under both circumstances.

moon   planet   meteoroids   comet   aurora borealis

c_____ ; ___

A a large cratered sphere in the sky

sometimes a crescent in the sky

m_____ ; ___

B a large sphere, made of gas or rock

a bright light in the sky that does not twinkle, seen clearly even in city-lit skies

m_____ ; ___

C a solar wind meeting gases in our atmosphere

a spectacular light show in the sky

a_____ ; ___

D has a nucleus, a coma, and a tail

a fuzzy, blurry, small blob with a tail

p_____ ; ___

E pieces of dark rock that contain iron

fast-moving streaks of light across the sky

Science Fact

While the Earth orbits the sun in about 365 days (that's one year for us), it takes Mercury only 88 Earth days. Neptune completes one revolution around the sun every 165 years!

21

The Moon

- From the Earth we only see the part of the moon that is lit up by the sun.
- Up close or through a telescope, we can see different features of the moon.

A.   Name the moon in different phases with "Crescent" or "Gibbous".   Then colour the part of the moon we see from the Earth yellow.

The moon orbits (travels around) the Earth, completing a revolution about once every month. As its position changes, the part of the moon that is lit by the sun also changes.

The Moon Phases*

* **Crescent** – appears as a thin crescent

Gibbous – means swollen on one side or humpbacked

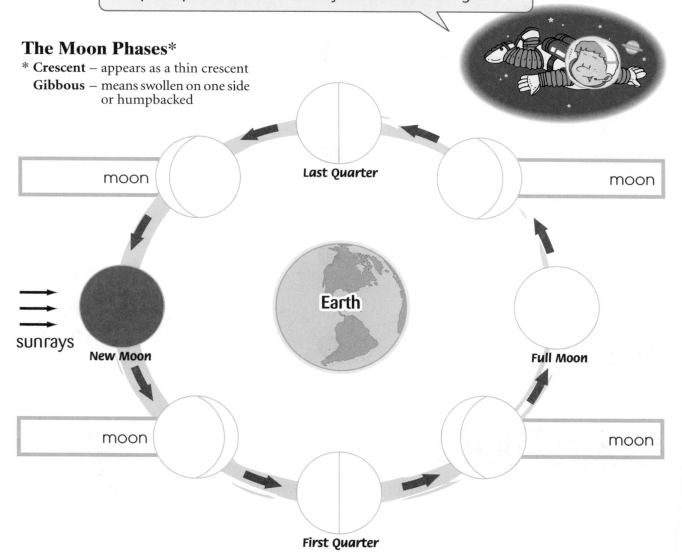

moon

Last Quarter

moon

sunrays

New Moon

Earth

Full Moon

moon

moon

First Quarter

B. **Fill in the blanks with the given words. Then label the diagram with "crater" and "maria".**

M_____ (meaning "seas") were once believed to be oceans on the surface of the moon. They are actually flat areas of the moon that appear dark compared to other mountainous or cratered areas. M_____ that crashed onto the moon's surface created c_____, another feature of the moon that can be seen from the Earth.

meteorites
craters
maria

The Moon

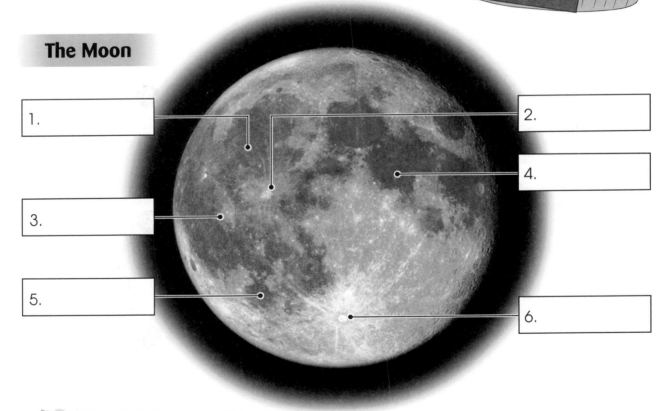

1. _____

2. _____

3. _____

4. _____

5. _____

6. _____

Science Fact

The dark and light features of the moon are caused not only by the shadows, but also by the moon's rocks which have dark and light colours.

22

Constellations

- Constellations are the stars in certain areas of the sky as we see them from the Earth. They are named for the shapes they appear to take when the brightest stars are joined by lines.
- Ancient people made up stories to explain the appearance of stars in the sky.

A. Trace the dotted lines and name the constellations. Then match them with the figures. Write the letters.

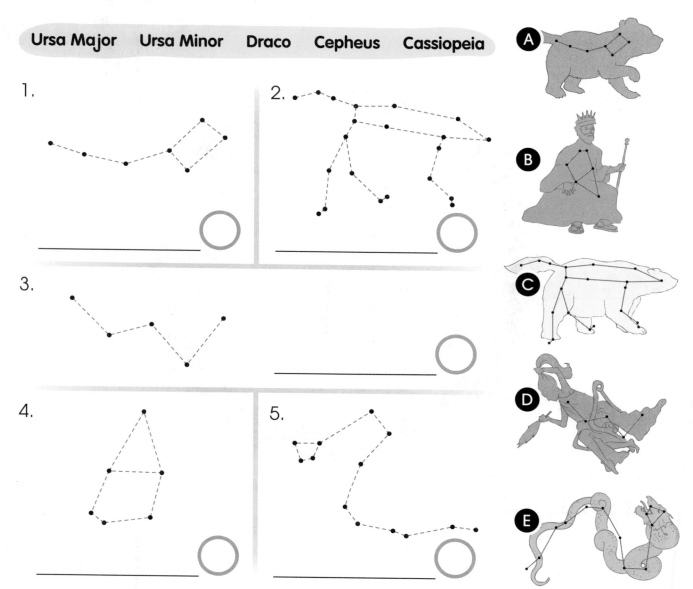

Ursa Major   Ursa Minor   Draco   Cepheus   Cassiopeia

1.

_____   ○

2.

_____   ○

3.

_____   ○

4.

_____   ○

5.

_____   ○

B. **Read the story about how Ursa Major (The Great Bear) and Ursa Minor (The Little Bear) came to be in the night sky. Then complete the diagram with the words in bold.**

Zeus was the king of all the gods. When he fell in love with beautiful Callisto, Zeus's wife Hera was enraged. She turned Callisto into a bear. Soon, Callisto's son Arcas came upon the bear while hunting in the forest. He readied his arrow, unaware that this bear was his mother. Just as Arcas was about to strike Callisto, King Zeus changed Arcas into a bear. Then, he grabbed them by their tails and flung them into the sky, where mother and son remain side-by-side forever. This is how Ursa Major, the big bear, and Ursa Minor, the little bear, came to be in the night sky.

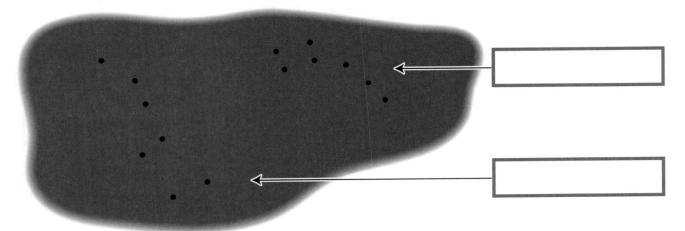

> The easily seen form of the **Big Dipper** is part of the constellation Ursa Major. Ursa Minor contains the star formation called the **Little Dipper**.

Little Dipper

Big Dipper

Connect the stars that form the Little Dipper and the Big Dipper. Then label them.

 Science Fact

Stars in the same constellation may be hundreds of light years away from one another. They appear to be close from our view on Earth, yet one may be much farther from us than another.

23

The Earth in Space

- It takes the Earth 24 hours to rotate around once. It is this rotation that gives us night and day.
- It takes about 365 days for the Earth to revolve around the sun. Because the Earth's axis is tilted, parts of the Earth get different amounts of sunlight through the year.

A. See how the Earth rotates in one day. Label each part of the Earth with the given words.

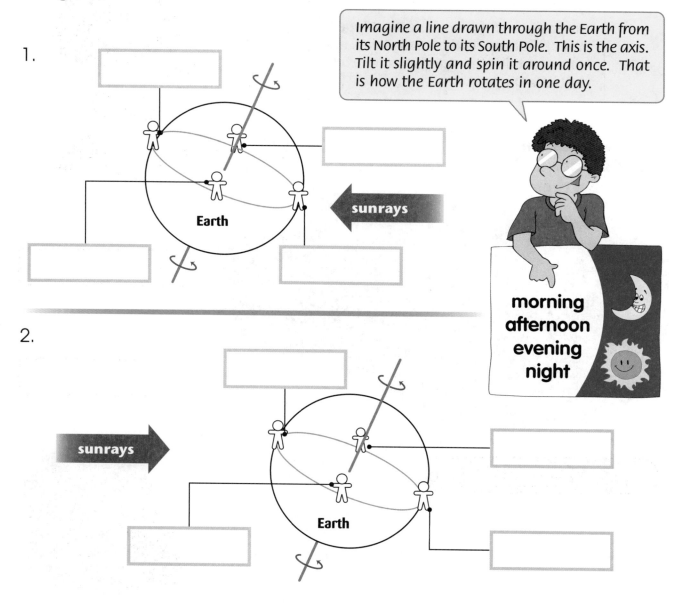

Imagine a line drawn through the Earth from its North Pole to its South Pole. This is the axis. Tilt it slightly and spin it around once. That is how the Earth rotates in one day.

morning
afternoon
evening
night

1.

Earth

sunrays

2.

sunrays

Earth

B.   Tell which seasons Canada has as the Earth revolves around the sun.

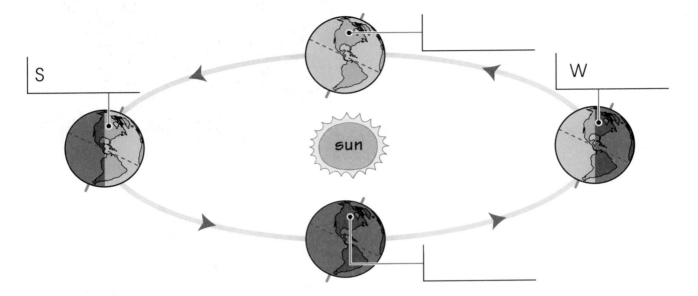

S

W

sun

Experiment

Things needed:

- 1 large melon or pumpkin
- 1 small orange

Place the melon on a bed. Roll the orange a short distance beside the melon. What happens?

The smaller orange is pulled toward the melon by gravity in the same way the Earth and all other planets are pulled into orbit around the sun. Larger bodies attract smaller bodies, with the amount of attraction dependent on the sizes of the bodies and their distance apart. Friction on the bed prevents the orange from going into orbit around the melon.

🧪 **Science Fact**

There are 24 hours in a day, but it takes the Earth about 23 hours, 56 minutes, and 4 seconds to do a complete rotation. That is why "leap seconds" are occasionally added to clocks worldwide.

24

Humans in Space

- Many satellites are orbiting the Earth right now – ones we have sent up to do specific jobs.
- The International Space Station was built as it was orbiting the Earth with the collective effort of many countries.

satellite

A.   Fill in the blanks with the correct words.

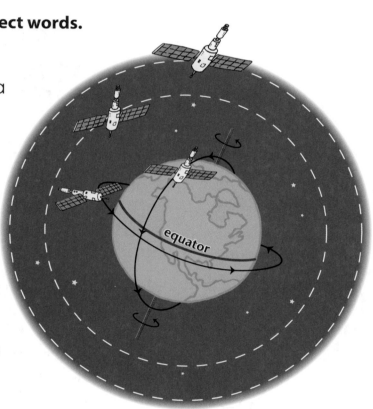

equator

1.   A map-making satellite has a

_____ orbit so it can
low/high

better view details of the

Earth.

2.   A satellite that follows the

Earth's rotation and stays

above the same part of

the Earth has an orbital path

over the _____ .
poles/equator

3.   Gravity is greater closer to the Earth,

and the greater the gravity, the faster a satellite must move. So, a

low-flying satellite moves _____ than a high-flying satellite.
faster/slower

4.   When two satellites are seen in the night sky, the one travelling at a

lower speed is in a _____ orbit.
higher/lower

B. **Fill in the blanks with the given words to complete the passage about the International Space Station. Then answer the questions.**

microgravity   muscles   space shuttles
experiments   orbit   astronauts   countries

Humans have been in the Earth's 1._____ constantly since the year 2000. Their home, the International Space Station, is so huge that it was built in stages while in orbit. 2._____ are used to send parts, supplies, and 3._____ , who spend up to six months on the station. While they are on the space station, astronauts perform 4._____ that cannot be performed on Earth. Their home has very little gravity, or 5._____ , which is an environment difficult to replicate on Earth. Because of the lack of gravity, astronauts have to work harder to keep their 6._____ strong. Many hours of their off-the-job time is spent on a treadmill. One of the most exciting things about the International Space Station is that it is a project of many different 7._____ of the world.

8. What is the home for humans in space?

   _____

9. Who are involved in the International Space Station project?

   _____

Science Fact

Canada is one of the countries involved in the International Space Station.

ANSWERS

1 Numbers to 1 000 000 (1)

1. Zone 1: $339 700   Zone 2: $463 400
   Zone 3: $328 400   Zone 4: $457 300
2. Zone 1: $448 865, $443 400, $339 700
   Zone 2: $674 900, $562 900, $556 680, $463 400
   Zone 3: $439 800, $337 480, $334 760, $328 400
   Zone 4: $560 280, $459 000, $457 300
3. The one that costs $674 900, which is in Zone 2
4. The one that costs $328 400, which is in Zone 3

5-6. (Suggested answers)

5. He should consider Zone 1 and Zone 2. He should consider the one that costs $448 865 in Zone 1 and the one that costs $562 900 in Zone 2.
6. He should consider Zone 3 and Zone 4. He should consider the one that costs $439 800 in Zone 3 and all the houses in Zone 4.
7. Old price: $337 480, $328 400, $439 800, $334 760
   New price: $336 480, $327 400, $438 800, $333 760
8. Old price: $560 280, $457 300, $459 000
   New price: $570 280, $467 300, $469 000
9. 300 000 + 40 000 + 5000 + 700 + 80 + 6
10. 600 000 + 70 000 + 5000 + 800 + 9
11. nine hundred one thousand eight hundred forty-three
12. two hundred sixty-three thousand four hundred eighty-one
13. 456 150 ; 603 048 ; 720 214 ; 296 507
14. a. 306 165   b. 430 094   c. 100 071
15. A: 300 000 ; 60 000 ; 4000 ; 200 ; 50 ; 9
    B: 400 000 ; 60 000 ; 1000 ; 500 ; 70 ; 3
    C: 700 000 ; 20 000 ; 1000 ; 300 ; 90 ; 8
16. a. B   b. C   c. C
17. 400 005, 400 050, 400 500, 405 000, 450 000, 500 004, 500 040, 500 400, 504 000, 540 000

2 Numbers to 1 000 000 (2)

1.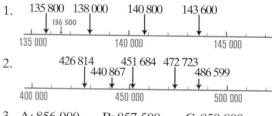
2.
3. A: 856 000   B: 857 500   C: 859 800
4. P: 608 000   Q: 625 000   R: 684 000
5. 391 111   393 333   395 555   397 777   399 999
   392 222   394 444   396 666   398 888
6. 227 222 ; 222 722

7.
475 000		790 000
480 000	580 000	680 000
485 000		570 000
490 000		460 000
495 000		

8. 208 453   9. 565 089
10. 7 ; 892 696, 892 697, 892 698, 892 699, 892 700, 892 701, 892 702
11. 5 ; 100 928, 100 930, 100 932, 100 934, 100 936
12. A: 400 000   B: 500 000
    C: 300 000   D: 600 000
    E: 600 000   F: 800 000
13. D and E   14. F
15. 500 000 ; 540 000   16. 700 000 ; 670 000
17. 800 000 ; 800 000   18. 400 000 ; 380 000
19. 400 000 ; 410 000   20. 800 000 ; 750 000
21. 1000 days – 10 000 L ;
    10 000 days – 100 000 L ;
    100 000 days – 1 000 000 L ;
    100 000 days
22. 1 000 000 hamburgers – 200 months ;
    200 months
23. 4 000 000 kg – 1000 elephants ;
    1 000 000 kg – 250 elephants ;
    250 elephants
24. 20 g – 1 treat
    200 g – 10 treats ;
    2 000 000 g – 100 000 treats ;
    1 000 000 g – 50 000 treats ;
    50 000 treats

3 Multiples and Factors

1. 18 ; 27 ; 36 ; 45 ; 54
   9, 18, 27, 36, 45, 54
2. 14 ; 21 ; 28 ; 35 ; 42
   7, 14, 21, 28, 35, 42
3. 24 ; 36 ; 48 ; 60 ; 72
   12, 24, 36, 48, 60, 72
4. 8: 8, 16, 24, 32, 40, 48, 56, 64, 72, 80
   2: 2, 4, 6, 8, 10, 12, 14, 16, 18, 20
   5: 5, 10, 15, 20, 25, 30, 35, 40, 45, 50
   11: 11, 22, 33, 44, 55, 66, 77, 88, 99, 110
5. 3 ; 6 ; 9 ; 12 ; 15 ; 18
   3, 6, 9, 12, 15, 18
6. 6 ; 12 ; 18 ; 24 ; 30 ; 36
   6, 12, 18, 24, 30, 36
7. 10 ; 20 ; 30 ; 40 ; 50 ; 60
   10, 20, 30, 40, 50, 60
8. 22, 66, 77   9. 6, 38, 42
10. 52, 64, 76, 84   11. 72, 80, 96
12. 10 ; 5 ; 1, 2, 5, 10   13. 15 ; 5 ; 1, 3, 5, 15

14. 18 ; 9 ; 6 ; 1, 2, 3, 6, 9, 18
15. 24 ; 12 ; 8 ; 6 ; 1, 2, 3, 4, 6, 8, 12, 24
16. 20 ; 10 ; 5 ; 1, 2, 4, 5, 10, 20
17. 27 ; 9 ; 1, 3, 9, 27
18. 9 = 1 x 9 ; = 3 x 3
    16 = 1 x 16 ; = 2 x 8 ; = 4 x 4
    17 = 1 x 17
    28 = 1 x 28 ; = 2 x 14 ; = 4 x 7
    30 = 1 x 30 ; = 2 x 15 ; = 3 x 10 ; = 5 x 6
    9: 1, 3, 9
    16: 1, 2, 4, 8, 16
    17: 1, 17
    28: 1, 2, 4, 7, 14, 28
    30: 1, 2, 3, 5, 6, 10, 15, 30
19. ✘ ; factors   20. ✔
21. ✘ ; 9   22. ✘ ; 12, 24, 36, and 48

4 Prime Numbers and Composite Numbers

1. Composite ; 20
   Prime ; 5
   1
2. 1, 2, 4, 8, 16 ; composite
3. 1, 7 ; prime
4. 1, 2, 3, 4, 6, 12 ; composite
5. 1, 2, 3, 6, 9, 18 ; composite
6.

✘	2	3	4	5	6	7	8	9	10
11	12	13	14	15	16	17	18	19	20
21	22	23	24	25	26	27	28	29	30
31	32	33	34	35	36	37	38	39	40
41	42	43	44	45	46	47	48	49	50
51	52	53	54	55	56	57	58	59	60
61	62	63	64	65	66	67	68	69	70
71	72	73	74	75	76	77	78	79	80
81	82	83	84	85	86	87	88	89	90
91	92	93	94	95	96	97	98	99	100

7. There are 25 prime numbers. They are 2, 3, 5, 7, 11, 13, 17, 19, 23, 29, 31, 37, 41, 43, 47, 53, 59, 61, 67, 71, 73, 79, 83, 89, and 97.
8. There are 36 composite numbers. They are 4, 6, 8, 9, 10, 12, 14, 15, 16, 18, 20, 21, 22, 24, 25, 26, 27, 28, 30, 32, 33, 34, 35, 36, 38, 39, 40, 42, 44, 45, 46, 48, 49, 50, 51, and 52.
9. 2   10. composite   11. 2
12.   13.

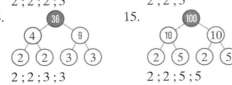

2 ; 2 ; 2 ; 5   2 ; 2 ; 5
14.   15.

2 ; 2 ; 3 ; 3   2 ; 2 ; 5 ; 5

16.   17.

2 ; 2 ; 2 ; 3   2 ; 3 ; 3 ; 3
18. **64** — 3 x 5 x 7
    105 — 2 x 3 x 3 x 5
    36 — 2 x 2 x 2 x 2 x 2 x 2
    90 — 2 x 2 x 3 x 3
    75 — 3 x 5 x 5
19. 2 ; 19   20. 2 ; 5 ; 5   21. 2 ; 2 ; 7
22. 3 ; 3 ; 5   23. 2 ; 2 ; 13   24. 2 ; 2 ; 3 ; 5
25. 2 x 5   26. 3 x 3 x 3 x 3
27. 2 x 2 x 2 x 7   28. 2 x 3 x 3 x 5
29. 7 x 13   30. 2 x 7
31. Yes   32. No

5 Addition and Subtraction of Whole Numbers

1. Mr. Smith's class: 42 645
   Mrs. Winter's class: 42 604
   Mrs. Gault's class: 46 003
   Ms. LeBlanc's class: 34 455
   Ms. Dottori's class: 43 425
   Mr. Wood's class: 35 717
   Mrs. McLellan's class: 36 235
   Ms. Carter's class: 58 495
   Mrs. Goldberger's class: 17 127
2. $584.95   3. Ms. Carter's class
4. 5 classes
5. 128 000 ; 128 528 ;

Estimate
```
  46000
+ 82000
 128000
```
Exact
```
  46382
+ 82146
 128528
```

6. 36 000 ; 35 764 ;

Estimate
```
  82000
- 46000
  36000
```
Exact
```
  82146
- 46382
  35764
```

7. 90 000 ; 89 760 ;

Estimate
```
  47000
+ 43000
  90000
```
Exact
```
  46583
+ 43177
  89760
```

8. 4000 ; 3406 ;

Estimate
```
  47000
- 43000
   4000
```
Exact
```
  46583
- 43177
   3406
```

9. 865 – 254 ; 611   10. 338 + 182 ; 520
11. 723 – 240 ; 483   12. 386 + 221 ; 607
13. 921 – 63 ; 858   14. 343 + 97 ; 440
15. 1054   16. 5089   17. 678
18. 520   19. – ; +   20. – ; –
21. + ; –
22. 27 546 + 34 668 ; 62 214 ; 62 214 points
23. 50 864 – 476 ; 50 388 ; 50 388 points

24. 7642 + (7642 − 827) ; 14 457 ; 14 457 points
25. 9476 − (475 + 475) ; 8526 ; 8526 points
26. 8000 − 255 ; 7745 ; 7745 points
27. 30 000 − 5 ; 29 995 ; 29 995 points

6   Multiplication of Whole Numbers

1.
```
    58
x   29
   522
  1160
  1682
```
2.
```
    63
x   47
   441
  2520
  2961
```
3.
```
    32
x   89
   288
  2560
  2848
```

4. 4736
5. 1961
6. 1849
7. 464
8. 3172
9. 2652
10. 1992
11. 385
12. 1274
13. 3648

14.
```
    2 6
x   2 5
  1 3 0
  5 2 0
  6 5 0
```
15.
```
    2 3
x   4 7
  1 6 1
  9 2 0
1 0 8 1
```

16.
```
    1 2 9
x     5 4
    5 1 6
  6 4 5 0
  6 9 6 6
```
17.
```
    4 9 6
x     6 7
  3 4 7 2
2 9 7 6 0
3 3 2 3 2
```

18.
```
    5 2 3
x     8 9
  4 7 0 7
4 1 8 4 0
4 6 5 4 7
```
19. 4968

20. 16 873
21. 51 282
22. 34 944
23. 4095
24. 11 704
25. 1740 ; 5365 candies ; 6235 candies
26. 4740 ; 7584 candies ; 13 272 candies
27. 8 ; 5 ; 40 ; 1080
28. 35 x 2 x 9 ; 70 x 9 ; 630
29. 6 x 5 x 23 ; 30 x 23 ; 690
30. 18 x 5 x 9 ; 90 x 9 ; 810
31. 14 x 5 x 63 ; 70 x 63 ; 4410
32. 75 x 4 x 19 ; 300 x 19 ; 5700
33. 6 x 88 x 15 = 6 x 15 x 88 = 90 x 88 = 7920 (g)
34. 6 x 9 x 145 = 6 x 145 x 9 = 870 x 9 = 7830 (mL)
35. 15 tins: 15 x 875 = 13 125 (g)
    138 boxes: 138 x 94 = 12 972 (g)
    15 tins of crackers
36. 25 big boxes: 25 x 144 = 3600 (pieces)
    38 small boxes: 38 x 96 = 3648 (pieces)
    38 small boxes
37. 36 boxes: 36 x 275 = 9900 (mL)
    14 bottles: 14 x 685 = 9590 (mL)
    Total: 9900 + 9590 = 19 490 (mL) ; 19 490 mL

7   Division of Whole Numbers

1.
```
      1 3 R 2 5
34 ) 4 6 7
     3 4
     1 2 7
     1 0 2
       2 5
```
2.
```
      8 R 2 0
69 ) 5 7 2
     5 5 2
       2 0
```

3.
```
      7 0 R 1
14 ) 9 8 1
     9 8
       1
```

4. 18
5. 17R27
6. 19R15
7. 18R7
8. 7R29
9. 12R19
10. 3R59
11. 12R28
12. a. 82   b. 24

13.
```
      2 3 6 R 6
16 ) 3 7 8 2
     3 2
       5 8
       4 8
       1 0 2
         9 6
           6
```
14.
```
      1 0 3 R 1
39 ) 4 0 1 8
     3 9
       1 1 8
       1 1 7
           1
```

15.
```
      8 5 R 3 4
95 ) 8 1 0 9
     7 6 0
       5 0 9
       4 7 5
         3 4
```
16. 72R46

17. 112R12
18. 50R13
19. 390
20. 81
21. 121R11
22. 107R18
23. 134R23
24. 68 lanes
25. $26
26. (400 + 40) ÷ 4: 110
    (250 + 55) ÷ 5: 61
    (800 − 72) ÷ 8: 91
    (770 − 7) ÷ 7: 109
    (66 + 42) ÷ 6: 18
27. 330 ÷ 3 + 45 ÷ 3 ; 110 + 15 ; 125
28. 360 ÷ 9 − 81 ÷ 9 ; 40 − 9 ; 31
29. 95   30. 191
31. 182   32. 101
33. 8240 ÷ 16 ; 515 ; 515 g
34. 3120 ÷ 15 ; 208 ; 208 chocolate eggs
35. 708 ÷ 12 ; 59 ; $59
36. 8448 ÷ 24 ; 352 ; 352 cm^2
37. 2000 ÷ 32 ; 62R16 ; 63 nets
38. 250 ÷ 78 ; 3R16 ; 3 pencils ; 16 pencils left

8   Operations with Whole Numbers

1. 26 614
2. 77 252
3.
```
      1 2 2 R 3 7
38 ) 4 6 7 3
     3 8
       8 7
       7 6
       1 1 3
         7 6
         3 7
```
4.
```
      3 4 7
x       6 8
    2 7 7 6
2 0 8 2 0
2 3 5 9 6
```

5.
```
    253
  x  19
   2277
   2530
   4807
```
6. 22 904

7. 11 097   8. 48 264   9. 244R17
10. 85 553   11. 7968   12. –
13. x   14. ÷   15. +
16.

54 293 + 27 886 → about 80 000
8025 ÷ 19 → about 400
116 x 59 → about 6000
893 x 28 → about 27 000
487 x 88 → about 45 000
3216 ÷ 31 → about 100
60 274 – 49 184 → about 10 000

17-18. (Suggested answers)
17. 26 000 ; 36 000   18. 20 000 ; 100
19. Check Strategy 1 and Strategy 3. ; 7614
20. Check Strategy 1 and Strategy 2. ; 122
21. (2772 – 900) ÷ 3 = 624 ; 624
22. (3 x 128) ÷ 4 = 96 ; 96
23. 56 ÷ 7 – 2 = 6 ; 6
24. 7 x 1245 + 608 = 9323 ; 9323

9   Perimeter and Area (1)

1. 46 mm / 28 mm
Perimeter:
46 ; 28 ; 148 ; mm
Area:
46 ; 28 ; 1288 ; mm²

2. 37 mm / 37 mm
Perimeter:
4 x 37 = 148 (mm)
Area:
37 x 37 = 1369 (mm²)

3. (Suggested drawings and answers)

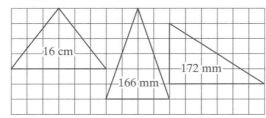

16 cm / 166 mm / 172 mm

4-7. (Individual answers)
8. triangle: 42 x 3 ; 126 ; m
   square: 34 x 4 ; 136 ; cm
   pentagon: 8 x 5 ; 40 ; m
   hexagon: 26 x 6 ; 156 ; cm
   octagon: 75 x 8 ; 600 ; mm
9. 16 x 7 ; 112 ; 112 cm
10. 12 x 14 ; 168 ; 168 mm

11. A: 96 cm   B: 88 mm   C: 85 cm
    D: 108 cm   E: 184 m   F: 420 mm
12. 58 cm

10   Perimeter and Area (2)

1. 9 cm / 7 cm   ; 9 ; 7 ; 63

2. 15 cm / 10 cm   ; 15 ; 10 ; 150

3. 18 cm / 6 cm   ; 18 ; 6 ; 108

4. A: 35 cm²   B: 980 cm²   C: 780 cm²
   D: 1104 mm²   E: 990 m²   F: 800 m²
   G: 1330 cm²   H: 1406 cm²

5.

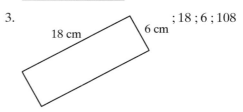

A: 5 ; 6 ; 30 ; 15
B: 5 x 4 ÷ 2 = 20 ÷ 2 = 10 (cm²)
C: 3 x 6 ÷ 2 = 18 ÷ 2 = 9 (cm²)
D: 6 x 5 ÷ 2 = 30 ÷ 2 = 15 (cm²)
E: 4 x 5 ÷ 2 = 20 ÷ 2 = 10 (cm²)
F: 2 x 5 ÷ 2 = 10 ÷ 2 = 5 (cm²)
6. a. 800 cm²   b. 124 cm
7. a. 315 cm²   b. 81 cm
8. a. 28 cm²   b. 48 cm
9. 720 cm²

11   Volume and Surface Area

1. 10 ; 3 ; 9 ; 270   2. 6 ; 6 ; 30 ; 1080
3. 27 ; 21 ; 45 ; 25 515
4. 11 x 7 ; 77 ; cm²
   77 x 18 ; 1386 ; cm³

5. $(7 \times 6 \div 2) \times 6 = 126$ (cm^2)
   $126 \times 9 = 1134$ (cm^3)
6. $12 \times 8 \div 2 = 48$ (cm^2)
   $48 \times 28 = 1344$ (cm^3)
7. $(16 \times 11 \div 2) \times 5 = 440$ (cm^2)
   $440 \times 30 = 13\ 200$ (cm^3)
8. 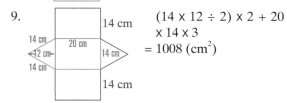 $6 \times 7 \times 2 + 15 \times 6 \times 2$
   $+ 15 \times 7 \times 2$
   $= 474$ (cm^2)

9. 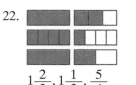 $(14 \times 12 \div 2) \times 2 + 20$
   $\times 14 \times 3$
   $= 1008$ (cm^2)

10. 592 cm^2 11. 96 cm^2 12. 1370 cm^2
13. $16 \times 15 \times 4 = 960$; 960 cm^3
14. $24 \times 18 \times 10 = 4320$; 4320 cm^3
15. a. $16 \times 15 \times 2 + 4 \times 16 \times 2 + 4 \times 15 \times 2 = 728$;
       728 cm^2
    b. $24 \times 18 \times 2 + 24 \times 10 \times 2 + 18 \times 10 \times 2 = 1704$;
       1704 cm^2
16. Volume $= (24 \times 16 \div 2) \times 36 + 24 \times 24 \times 36$
           $= 27\ 648$ (cm^3)
    Surface area $= (24 \times 16 \div 2) \times 2 + 20 \times 36 \times 2$
                 $+ 24 \times 24 \times 2 + 36 \times 24 \times 2 + 24$
                 $\times 36$
                 $= 5568$ (cm^2)

12 Fractions

1. $\frac{4}{8}$ 2. $\frac{5}{12}$ 3. $\frac{11}{18}$
4. $\frac{46}{10}$; $4\frac{6}{10}$ 5. $\frac{21}{4}$; $5\frac{1}{4}$
6. $\frac{16}{6}$; $2\frac{4}{6}$ 7. $\frac{10}{7}$; $1\frac{3}{7}$
8.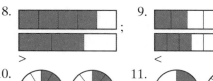
9.
   >   <
10.
11.
   >   <
12. 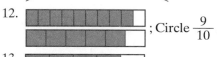 ; Circle $\frac{9}{10}$.
13. 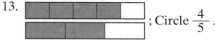 ; Circle $\frac{4}{5}$.

14.  ; Circle $\frac{5}{8}$.
15. ; Circle $\frac{3}{4}$.
16. $4\frac{9}{10}$ 17. $3\frac{4}{5}$ 18. $7\frac{2}{3}$
19. $5\frac{2}{3}$ 20. $1\frac{1}{2}$ 21. $2\frac{5}{6}$
22. 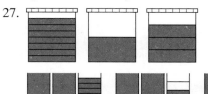 23.
    $1\frac{2}{3}, 1\frac{1}{2}, \frac{5}{4}$ $1\frac{3}{5}, \frac{3}{2}, 1\frac{1}{3}$
24. $\frac{5}{6}$ 25. $\frac{7}{9}$ 26. $\frac{9}{6}$
27.

28. $\frac{7}{8}$ kg of flour and $2\frac{1}{3}$ kg of sugar

13 Decimals

1. 2.952 ; 2 ; 952   2. 1.036 ; 1 ; 36
3. 4.062   4. 6.005
5. 3.123   6. 10.004
7. 5 and 273 thousandths
8. 3 and 18 thousandths
9. 8 and 176 thousandths
10. 7 and 9 thousandths
11. 0.9   12. 0.08   13. 0.2
14. 0.008   15. 7   16. 0.06
17. 0.06   18. 0.008   19. 0.5
20. 0.07
21. 0.020   0.222
     0.222   0.022
     0.022   0.02
     0.202   0.22
     0.220   0.202
22. 2.499 ; 2.500 ; 2.503
23. 60.801 ; 60.800 ; 60.799
24. 5.283 ; 5.293 ; 5.303
25. 8.195 ; 8.200 ; 8.210
26. 9.074 ; 8.974 ; 8.774

27.

C ; 3.986 m

28.

C ; 8.253 L

29.

D ; 5.22 kg

30. 6 ; 6.3 ; 6.27   31. 10 ; 10.2 ; 10.17
32. 8 ; 7.6 ; 7.59   33. 6 ; 6.4 ; 6.41
34. 9 ; 9.0 ; 9.00   35. 13 ; 13.0 ; 12.95
36. 3.284, 5.598   37. 3.284, 6.886
38. 3.264, 5.578, 6.714, 6.741, 6.866, 6.986, 7.238

14 Addition and Subtraction of Decimals

1.
```
  4.574
+ 2.653
  7.227
```
2.
```
  8.654
- 3.48
  5.174
```
3.
```
  29.6
- 12.864
  16.736
```
4.
```
  9.68
+ 5.279
  14.959
```
5.
```
  10.004
- 7.37
  2.634
```
6.
```
  0.187
+ 8.66
  8.847
```
7. 11.973   8. 5.059   9. 17.137
10. 9.067   11. 17.961   12. 5.377
13. 5.136   14. 6.437   15. 2.014
16. 3.609   17. 2.269
18-20. (Individual estimates)
18.
```
  3.125        3.125
+ 2.08       - 2.08
  5.205        1.045
```
19.
```
  4.125        4.125
+ 0.75       - 0.75
  4.875        3.375
```
20.
```
  9.524        9.524
+ 8.9        - 8.9
  18.424       0.624
```
21. ✗   22. ✔   23. ✗
24. ✔   25. ✔   26. ✔
27.
```
  5.893
+ 7.588
  13.481
```
28.
```
  9.633
- 4.159
  5.474
```
29.
```
  12.804
-  9.157
   3.647
```
30.
```
  9.381
- 4.673
  4.708
```
31.
```
  7.693
+ 6.257
  13.950
```
32.
```
  2.583
+ 9.707
  12.290
```

33. a. 48.72 kg ; 44.618 kg
    b. 4.102 kg
34. a. 1.418 m   b. 0.738 m   c. 0.642 m
35. 3.593 + 4.082 ; 7.675 ; 7.675 kg
36. 1.534 + 0.66 ; 2.194 ; 2.194 km
37. 10 – 4.186 ; 5.814 ; 5.814 m
38. 2.64 – 1.374 ; 1.266 ; 1.266 L
39. John: 1.302   Eva: 1.777
    Tina: 1.069   Leo: 1.906
40. John

15 Multiplication and Division of Decimals

1. 15.6   2. 2.4   3. 8.7
4. 79.2   5. 43.2   6. 48.5
7. 105.6   8. 127.2   9. 65.4
10. 39.2   11. 73.5   12. 4.8
13.
```
      1.6
  6 ) 9.6
      6
      36
      36
```
14.
```
      6.4
  7 ) 44.8
      42
      28
      28
```
15.
```
      12.5
  6 ) 75.0
      6
      15
      12
      30
      30
```
16.
```
      2.3
  18 ) 41.4
       36
       54
       54
```
17.
```
       10.9
  16 ) 174.4
       16
       144
       144
```
18.
```
        15.5
  28 ) 434.0
       28
       154
       140
       140
       140
```
19. 7.4   20. 19.5   21. 7.8
22. 11.6   23. 74.4 ÷ 6 ; 12.4 ; 12.4 L
24. ✗ ; 0.94   25. ✔   26. ✗ ; 8.6
27. ✔   28. ✔   29. ✔
30. ✔   31. ✗ ; 0.05
32. 4 ; 40 ; 400 ; 4000
33. 85 ; 850 ; 8500 ; 85 000
34. 137 ; 1370 ; 13 700 ; 137 000
35. 2006 ; 20 060 ; 200 600 ; 2 006 000
36. 0.36 ; 0.036 ; 0.0036 ; 0.00036
37. 1.05 ; 0.105 ; 0.0105 ; 0.00105
38. a. 1.2 ÷ 6 ; 0.2 ; 0.2 kg
    b. 1.2 x 9 ; 10.8 ; 10.8 kg
39. a. 16 x 18.7 ; 299.2 ; 299.2 cm^2
    b. 299.2 ÷ 2 ; 149.6 ; 149.6 cm^2
40. 1.8 ÷ 6 ; 0.3 ; 0.3 kg

16 Fractions, Decimals, and Percents

1. A: 43 out of 100, forty-three percent, or 43%
   B: 68 out of 100, sixty-eight percent, or 68%
   C: 44 out of 100, forty-four percent, or 44%
   D: 50 out of 100, fifty percent, or 50%

2. 3. 4.

5. (Suggested answers)
   A: 50%   B: 20%   C: 95%
   D: 10%   E: 80%   F: 60%

6. chickens: 25%   pigs: 35%
   cows: 12%   horses: 8%
   ducks: 20%   4-legged animals: 55%
   2-legged animals: 45%

7. (Colour as instructed) 57%

8. $\frac{40}{100}$; $\frac{2}{5}$ 9. $\frac{95}{100}$; $\frac{19}{20}$ 10. $\frac{54}{100}$; $\frac{27}{50}$

11. $\frac{75}{100}$; $\frac{3}{4}$ 12. $\frac{66}{100}$; $\frac{33}{50}$ 13. $\frac{84}{100}$; $\frac{21}{25}$

14. $\frac{25}{100}$; 0.25   15. $\frac{96}{100}$; 0.96   16. $\frac{48}{100}$; 0.48

17. $\frac{65}{100}$; 0.65   18. $\frac{84}{100}$; 0.84   19. $\frac{70}{100}$; 0.7

20. 27   21. 62%   22. 50%
23. 39   24. 91%   25. 16%
26. A, C   27. B, C   28. A, B
29. B, C

17 Unit Rates and Ratios

1. 4 ; 8 ; 0.5
2. 750 mL ÷ 3 boxes ; 250 mL/box
3. 882 g ÷ 7 apples ; 126 g/apple
4. 360 g ÷ 30 treats ; 12 g/treat
5. 98   6. 153 robots/day
7. 14 pencils/child   8. 189.6 kg/bag
9. 25 light bulbs/box   10. 5.5 km/h
11. A: 0.82   B: $0.69/can
    C: $0.79/can ; B
12. A: $2.65   B: $2.78/bottle
    C: $2.63/bottle ; C
13. A: 4.77   B: $5.12/key chain
    C: $4.69/key chain ; C
14. a. 13.50   b. 12.80
15. a. 40   b. 32
16. a. 24:10   b. 16:24
    c. 10:50
17. a. 4:6   b. 4:10
    c. 2:8   d. 3:7
18. a. 4:64   b. 4:68   c. 28:40

19. 2:3, 8:12   20. 3:9, 1:3   21. 4:5, 8:10
22. 1:4   23. 2:3   24. 1:2
25. 1:2   26. 3:5   27. 2:13
28.   a. 1:2
                                     b. 1:6

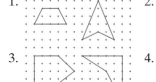

29. 3:4

18 Unit Conversions

1. 3016 ;

kg			g		
3	0	1	6		

2. 4300 ;

g			mg		
4	3	0	0		

3. 5620 ;

kg			g		
5	6	2	0		

4. 8025 ;

g			mg		
8	0	2	5		

5. 2016 ;

km			m		
2	0	1	6		

6. 316 ;

m		cm	
3	1	6	

7. 75 ;

cm	mm	
7	5	

8. 5009 ;

km			m		
5	0	0	9		

9. 1025 ;

L			mL		
1	0	2	5		

10. 3600 ;

L			mL		
3	6	0	0		

11. 1.06 ; 1060 g   12. 2.39 ; 239 cm
13. 2.75 ; 2750 mL   14. 3.28 ; 3280 m
15. 4.9 ; 49 mm   16. 0.3 ; 300 mL
17. 5065 ; 5.065 kg   18. 3925 ; 3.925 L
19. 866 ; 0.866 km   20. 72 ; 0.72 m
21. 480 ; 0.48 kg   22. 67 ; 6.7 cm
23. A: 9030   B: 9500
    From heaviest to lightest: B, C, A
24. A: 190   B: 187.6
    From tallest to shortest: A, C, B
25. A: 18.584   B: 92.085
    From greatest capacity to least capacity: C, B, A
26. 8039 mL   27. 70 086 m   28. 82 mm
29. 40 m 19 cm 30. 1763 m   31. 90 024 g
32. 1500 ÷ 6 = 250 ; 250
33. 5 × 570 = 2850 ;
    She needs 2850 mL of paint to paint 5 doors.
34. 18.2 + 20.9 = 39.1 ;
    The height of the rocket is 39.1 cm.
35. 126 – 19 = 107 ;
    Ivan is 107 cm long.

19 2-D Shapes (1)

1-4. (Suggested answers)

1.   2.

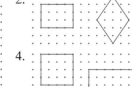

3.   4.

5.

6.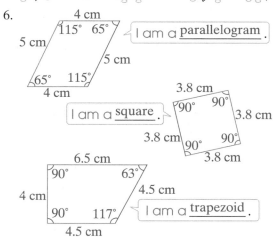

   4 cm

  115° 65° — I am a <u>parallelogram</u>.

5 cm   5 cm

 65° 115°

  4 cm

3.8 cm

I am a <u>square</u>.   90°   90°   3.8 cm

3.8 cm   90°   90°

   3.8 cm

  6.5 cm

90°   63°

4 cm   4.5 cm

90°   117° — I am a <u>trapezoid</u>.

  4.5 cm

   5.6 cm

I am a <u>rectangle</u>.   90°   90°

  3.2 cm   3.2 cm

  90°   90°

   5.6 cm

 3.7 cm

60° 120°   3.7 cm

3.7 cm   120° 60° — I am a <u>rhombus</u>.

  3.7 cm

7. a. square, rectangle
  b. parallelogram, rhombus, square, rectangle
  c. parallelogram, rhombus, square, rectangle
  d. trapezoid

8.   9.

10.

11. A, B, C, D, F   12. 4

13. 2   14. 5   15. 6

16.

A	B	C	D	E
✔	✘	✔	✘	✔
3		4		1
✔	✔	✔	✔	✘
3	2	4	2	

17. (Suggested drawings)

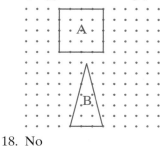

18. No

20 2-D Shapes (2)

1. The hexagon: ∠A: 110° ; an obtuse
                 ∠B: 110° ; an obtuse angle
                 ∠C: 140° ; an obtuse angle
                 ∠D: 110° ; an obtuse angle
                 ∠E: 110° ; an obtuse angle
                 ∠F: 140° ; an obtuse angle
   The triangle: ∠P : 23° ; an acute
                 ∠Q : 22° ; an acute angle
                 ∠R: 135° ; an obtuse angle
   The pentagon: ∠S: 90° ; a right
                 ∠T: 135° ; an obtuse angle
                 ∠U: 90° ; a right angle
                 ∠V: 120° ; an obtuse angle
                 ∠W: 105° ; an obtuse angle

2. 117° ;   3. 39° ;
  an obtuse angle ;   an acute angle ;

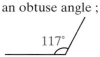

4. 90° ;   5. 180° ;
  a right angle ;   a straight angle ;

6.   7.

8.   9.

10.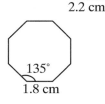

11. A: 65° ; 65° ; 180°   B: 73° ; 33° ; 180°
    C: 37° ; 27° ; 180°

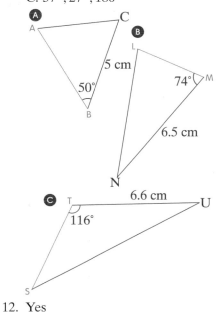

12. Yes

21 3-D Figures

1.

5. a.
   top view   side view   front view

   b.
   top view   side view   front view

   c.
   top view   side view   front view

   d.
   top view   side view   front view

6. B   7. E   8. A

9.
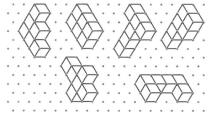

10. (Suggested drawings)

11.
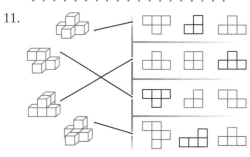

12.   13.

22 Transformations

1. fixed ; congruent   2. C
3. B   4. B
5. counterclockwise rotation of 90°
6. rotation of 180°
7. clockwise rotation of 90°
8. counterclockwise rotation of 90°
9.
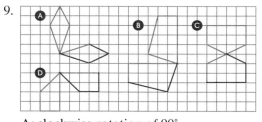

A: clockwise rotation of 90°
B: counterclockwise rotation of 90°
C: rotation of 180°
D: counterclockwise rotation of 90°

10.

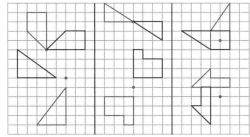

11.

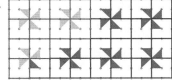

12.

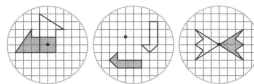

rotation and translation

13.

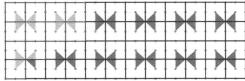

reflection and translation

14.

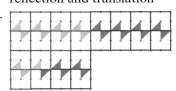

rotation and translation

23 Coordinate System

1. a. 6   b. 1   c. 6
   d. 0   e. 2   f. 0
   g. 2   h. 2
2. 2 ; the bear, the cow
3. 1 ; the monkey
4. 🐟 :(1,0), (1,5), (3,3), (3,5), (4,3), (6,0), (7,6), (9,3), (10,5), (11,2)
   🐟 :(1,3), (2,1), (4,2), (5,1), (5,6), (6,4), (8,0), (11,0)
   🦈 : (0,2), (0,4), (5,3), (8,2), (9,1), (11,4)
5. the fish at (10,5)   6. the fish at (2,1)
7. the shark at (9,1)
8. The shark at (5,3) will eat the most fish. It will get 3 fish.

9.

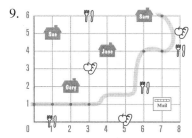

10. (0,1), (1,1), (2,1), (3,1), (6,4), (7,4), (7,6)
11. Sue: the one at (1,1) ; Sam: the one at (7,6) ; Gary: the one at (2,1) ; Jane: the one at (6,4)
12. He should get off the bus at (7,4), and then walks 3 squares down to the mall.

13.

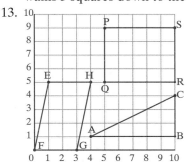

14. Stage 1: triangle ; 9
    Stage 2: rectangle ; 20
    Stage 3: parallelogram ; 15
15. 540 units

24 Patterning

1.

1, 3, 5, 7, 9, 11, 13   2. 49, 36, 25, 16, 9, 4

3.

5, 7, 9, 11, 13, 15
4. a. Start with 1 and add 2 each time to get the next term.
   b. 31   c. the 20th
5. a. Start with 120 and subtract 4 each time to get the next term.
   b. 76   c. the 21st
6. a. Start with 2 and multiply by 2 each time to get the next term.
   b. 1024   c. the 14th
7. a. Start with 24 576 and divided by 2 each time to get the next term.
   b. 48   c. the 12th

8.

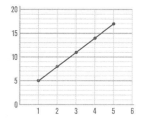

Term number	Term	Ordered pairs
1	5	(1,5)
2	8	(2,8)
3	11	(3,11)
4	14	(4,14)
5	17	(5,17)

20

9.

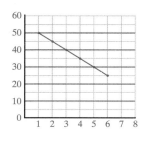

Term number	Term	Ordered pairs
1	50	(1,50)
2	45	(2,45)
3	40	(3,40)
4	35	(4,35)
5	30	(5,30)
6	25	(6,25)

8

10.

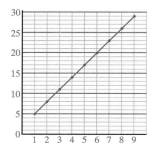

Term number	Term	Ordered pairs
1	5	(1,5)
2	8	(2,8)
3	11	(3,11)
4	14	(4,14)
5	17	(5,17)
6	20	(6,20)
7	23	(7,23)
8	26	(8,26)
9	29	(9,29)

29

11.

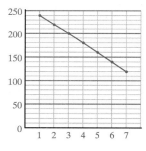

Term number	Term	Ordered pairs
1	240	(1,240)
2	220	(2,220)
3	200	(3,200)
4	180	(4,180)
5	160	(5,160)
6	140	(6,140)
7	120	(7,120)

120

25 Simple Equations

1. $A = (b \times h) \div 2$
   a. 10 ; 8 ; 40   b. 12 ; 20 ; 120
2. $C = \$100 - \$9 \times y$
   a. 8 ; = $28   b. $C = \$100 - \$9 \times 11$
                         = $1
3. $N = 20 \times m + 8 \times n$
   a. $N = 20 \times 3 + 8 \times 1$ b. $N = 20 \times 2 + 8 \times 6$
       = 68   = 88
4. 11 ; 20 ; 9   5. $70 \div x = 10 ; x = 7$
6. $40 - x = 35 ; x = 5$ 7. $x \times 24 = 48 ; x = 2$
8. $x + 9 = 25 ; x = 16$
9. $k + 3 + y = 9 ; 9 + y = 9 ; y = 0$
10. $y + u - 6 = 16 ; y + 10 = 16 ; y = 6$
11. $b \times 6 - y = 4 ; 12 - y = 4 ; y = 8$
12. $y \div 3 = 9 ; y = 27$

13. 41   14. 7   15. 72
16. 5   17. 32   18. 14
19. 11   20. 14   21. 2
22. a. $20 - n$
    b. $4 = 20 - n ; n = 16$; 16 party hats used
23. a. $y \times 6$
    b. $96 = y \times 6 ; y = 16$; 16 guests
24-29. (Individual testing)
   24. 6   25. 360   26. 7
   27. 30   28. 4   29. 8
   30. $26 + 4 \times c = 50 ; c = 6$; 6

26 Graphs (1)

1. X-Mart Fertilizer   2. 32 cm
3. 38 cm
4. Amazing Fertilizer, because it was even worse than using no fertilizer.
5. a. 13 cm   b. 8 cm
6. a. A   b. B   c. B
7. a. X-Mart Fertilizer: 2.50 ; 54
      Texas Fertilizer: 1.80 ; 38
      Joe's Club Fertilizer: 1.90 ; 52
   b. Joe's Club Fertilizer, because it is the most cost effective. It is almost as effective as X-Mart Fertilizer, which is the most effective, but is only a bit more expensive than Texas Fertilizer, which is the cheapest.
8. 2:00 p.m.   9. 27°C   10. about 34°C
11. The temperature rose from 18°C to 36°C.
12. The temperature dropped from 36°C to 30°C.
13. 12°C
14. Week 4. The data should be 75 apple pies made and 60 apple pies sold.
15. 30 ; 20 ; 15 ; 15 ; 10 ; 20 ; 20 ; 10 ; 5 ; 10
16. Week 9
17. (Individual answer)

27 Graphs (2)

1. bar graph   2. continuous line graph
3. broken-line graph   4. stem-and-leaf plot
5. double bar graph   6. pictograph
7. continuous line graph
8. broken-line graph
9.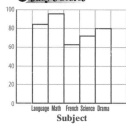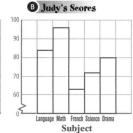

10. 79   11. Math

12. A: Start at 0, in the multiples of 20
    B: Start at 60, in the multiples of 10

13. B, because it shows that her score in Math is much higher than the scores in other subjects.

14. A, because it shows that the scores of all her subjects are pretty close to one another.

15.
Time Spent (h) on the Internet Last Week

Stem	Leaves
0	1 3 4 5 8 8 8 9 9
1	0 2 2 2 2 3 4 8
2	0 2
4	0

16.
Time Spent (h) on the Internet Last Week

Stem	Leaves
0	4 6 6 7 8 8 8 9 9
1	0 2 2 2 3 3 3 4 4 6 6 6 6 7 8 8 8 9
2	0 0 0 1 1 1 4 4 5 6 8 8 9 9 9
3	0 0 0 2 2 2 3 4

17.
Time Spent (h) on the Internet Last Week

Stem	Leaves
0	1 3 4 4 5 6 6 7 8 8 8 8 8 8 9 9 9 9
1	0 0 2 2 2 2 2 2 2 3 3 3 3 4 4 4 6 6 6 6 7 8 8 8 8 9
2	0 0 0 0 1 1 1 2 4 4 5 6 8 8 9 9 9
3	0 0 0 2 2 2 3 4
4	0

18. Ray's data: 12 h ; 11 h ; 12 h ; 39 h
    Tina's data: 19 h ; 18 h ; 16 h ; 30 h
    Ray & Tina's data: 17 h ; 16 h ; 12 h ; 39 h

19. Ray's data: The range is big. Since the mean, median, and mode are close, it shows that most children did not spend too much time on the Internet.
    Tina's data: The range is small. Since the mean, median, and mode are about 20 h, most children spent about the same time on the Internet.
    Ray & Tina's data: It has a wide range. This set of data spreads out evenly around the mean: 17 h.

20. The combined set of Ray and Tina's data is the best to represent a large population because it is a larger sample set and the data in this set is distributed evenly with the mean and median near the middle of the range.

28 Probability

1. cookie, milk, muffin, yogourt
    a. $\frac{1}{4}$ b. $\frac{1}{4}$ c. $\frac{2}{4}$ or $\frac{1}{2}$

2. 1, 2, 3, 4, 5, 6
    a. $\frac{1}{6}$ b. $\frac{2}{6}$ or $\frac{1}{3}$ c. $\frac{3}{6}$ or $\frac{1}{2}$
    d. $\frac{3}{6}$ or $\frac{1}{2}$ e. 0

3. a. $\frac{4}{5}$ b. 0   c. $\frac{1}{50}$

4. a. $\frac{3}{16}$ b. $\frac{3}{5}$ c. $\frac{1}{40}$

5. a. $\frac{2}{15}$ b. $\frac{2}{3}$

6-7. (Suggested answers for predictions)

6. apple: $\frac{1}{3}$; 15 ; 34

    orange: $\frac{1}{9}$; about 6 times ; about 11 times

    banana: $\frac{2}{9}$; about 11 times ; about 22 times

    strawberry: $\frac{1}{9}$; about 6 times ; about 11 times

    pear: $\frac{1}{9}$; about 6 times ; about 11 times

    watermelon: $\frac{1}{9}$; about 6 times ; about 11 times

7. cat: $\frac{3}{8}$; 15 ; 38

    pig: $\frac{1}{8}$; about 5 times ; about 12 times

    dog: $\frac{1}{4}$; about 10 times ; about 26 times

    cow: $\frac{1}{8}$; about 5 times ; about 12 times

    bird: $\frac{1}{8}$; about 5 times ; about 12 times

8. ; C

Frequency	Fraction
25 times	$\frac{25}{100} = \frac{1}{4}$
24 times	$\frac{24}{100} = \frac{6}{25}$
25 times	$\frac{25}{100} = \frac{1}{4}$
26 times	$\frac{26}{100} = \frac{13}{50}$

; B

Frequency	Fraction
16 times	$\frac{16}{100} = \frac{4}{25}$
34 times	$\frac{34}{100} = \frac{17}{50}$
50 times	$\frac{50}{100} = \frac{1}{2}$

; A

Frequency	Fraction
48 times	$\frac{48}{100} = \frac{12}{25}$
36 times	$\frac{36}{100} = \frac{9}{25}$
16 times	$\frac{16}{100} = \frac{4}{25}$

; D

Frequency	Fraction
43 times	$\frac{43}{100}$
19 times	$\frac{19}{100}$
18 times	$\frac{18}{100} = \frac{9}{50}$
20 times	$\frac{20}{100} = \frac{1}{5}$

1 The Big Five of the Safari

A. 1. like to wander alone at night
2. must always be approached with caution
3. the most dangerous of all African animals
4. can get rather grumpy and unpredictable
5. sleep with their "pride"

B. 4 ; 2 ; 5 ; 1 ; 3

C. 1. carnivores
2. beasts
3. keen
4. borrowed
5. Swahili
6. journey

D. 1. (elephants) ; Africa ; Antarctica
2. English (safari) Big Five
3. (continent) Bernie ; the Mediterranean Sea
4. Swahili (speed) Marie ; King of the Beasts
5. (travellers) ; Mr. Ross ; (fierceness) ; Egyptians

E. 1. Europe
2. sense
3. Canadian English
4. kilograms

F. 1. C   2. A
3. A   4. A
5. C   6. A

G. (Individual writing)

2 Nkosi Johnson

A. 1. JOHNSON
2. YOUNG
3. FOSTER MOTHER
4. SOUTH AFRICA
5. PREGNANT
6. BABIES
7. AIDS CARE CENTRE
8. HIV
9. STRONG
10. FIGHTING
11. SPEECHES
human beings

B. 1. (sick) ; mother
2. (care) ; centre
3. (biological) (AIDS-related) ; mother ; illness

4. (foster) (volunteer) ; mother ; worker
5. (human) (easy) ; beings ; acceptance
6. care ; volunteer

C. (Individual writing)

D. 1. her   2. its
3. Your   4. its
5. his   6. our/my
7. my   8. their/her

E. (Individual writing)

3 National Child Day

A. (Suggested definitions and individual writing of sentences)
1. high regard felt or shown towards a person
2. knowledge
3. written or printed record of something important
4. encourage something by making it public
5. confirmed by formal consent or signature

B. (Individual answers)

C. 1. T ; smiles
2. I
3. T ; Bill C-371
4. T ; November 20
5. T ; rights
6. T ; awareness
7. I

D. (Individual writing)

E. 1. may   2. Can
3. has to   4. did
5. can   6. may
7. do   8. May

F. (Individual writing of sentences)
I notice that "do" needs to be changed to "does", but "can" stays the same.

4 The History of Mauve

A. 1. B   2. A
3. C   4. C
5. B

B. 1. primary
    2. pastel
    3. process
    4. prevention
    5. purplish
    6. produce
C. 1. partly
    2. soundly
    3. rather
    4. any
    5. really
    6. too
    7. fully
    8. almost
D. 1. artificially ; most ; very ; historically
    2. substantially ; already ; later ; actually ; accidentally
    3. really ; so ; not ; hard ; still ; not ; affordably ; today
E. 1. You're a fast walker. Do you walk this <u>fast</u> all the time?
    2. Keri was the first one to finish. She gets to go <u>first</u> in the next round.
    3. This is a far cry from what I ever expected of you! It seems like you will go very <u>far</u> in architecture.
    4. The same word is used as an adjective and as an adverb.

5 The Group of Seven

A. 1. T   2. F
    3. T   4. T
    5. F
B. 1. In the beginning, critics scoffed at their work.
    2. For these artists, the rugged country inspired them not only with respect to their paintings, but also with respect to life.
    3. Canada consists of 3 500 523 square miles of mostly landscape. It is apparently intended to be the home of broadminded people.
    4. The more you know, the less you condemn.
C. 1. were
    2. portray ; it
    3. is ; his
    4. her ; gets

5. is ; her
6. looks ; These
7. that ; my
D. 1. "If critics are known by the company they keep, are we then known by the friends we have?" Julie asks her dad.
    2. Whatever you decide to do, make sure you are brave enough to confront the unexpected.
    3. When we say "A rose by any other name will smell as sweet", we are saying that something will still be the same even if we give it a different name.
E. (Individual writing)

6 Planet "Chanyikhei"

A.
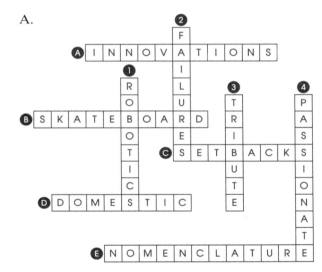

B. 1. object
    2. subject
    3. subject
    4. object
    5. object
C. 1. Mrs. Forrester ; ✔
    2.
    3. a needy family ; ✔
    4. her cousin ; ✔
    5.
D. (Individual answers)
E. (Individual writing)

7 Too Nice to Be Forgotten

A.

u	N	o	M	a	n	h	a	t	t	a	n	K	a	r	e	n
p	e	l	P	H	o	n	g		K	o	n	g	j	o	b	N
r	w	a	e	y	C	b	u	s	i	n	e	s	s	C	h	e
o		w	t	t	h	p	u	b	l	i	s	h	e	r	s	w
j	Y	y	r	i	i	W	o	r	l	d		T	r	a	d	e
e	o	e	i	c	n	e	c	o	m	p	u	t	e	r	s	Y
c	r	r	n	m	a	n	u	s	c	r	i	p	t	A	r	o
t	e	d	u	c	a	t	i	o	n	a	C	e	n	t	e	r

B. 1. Terrorists attacked the World Trade Center, killing 3000 people.
   2. Frankie felt he should do something more with his life. He left his job, returned to Hong Kong, and pursued his dream of starting an educational software company to help children.
   3. It is both a tribute to Frankie and proof of his family's love and strong spirit during their most difficult time.

C. 1. Ariel and Petrina called it "Wishing Daddy to Come Home". ; D
   2. The local publishers returned the manuscript to them, but the book ended up selling out its first print run. ; I
   3. He was a cool dad, living and working as a busy lawyer in one of the world's most dynamic cities. ; S
   4. Has Ella told it to you? ; D

D. Frankie decided he should pursue his dream after that fateful morning of September 11, 2001. Two years later, his new educational software company was well on its way to China when another tragedy struck, and this time Frankie became a victim himself. His daughters were scared, but were nevertheless inspired by their father's do-good example. They kept themselves strong in spirit. Their mother stayed strong herself as well. They wrote Frankie poems and made him drawings while he was in hospital. They continued to write after his death, putting together a book that was their tribute to him, selling out its first print run. Although a wife has lost her husband and two young daughters have lost their father, this family has shown us that staying strong is possible even when it seems impossible to do so.

E. (Individual writing)

8 The Seven Wonders of the Ancient World

A. 1. The Temple of Artemis at Ephesus
   2. The Statue of Zeus at Olympia
   3. The Hanging Gardens of Babylon
   4. The Colossus of Rhodes
   5. The Great Pyramid of Giza

B. (Individual writing)

C. 1. A   2. B
   3. A   4. B
   5. B

D. 1. which
   2. What
   3. one another
   4. Which
   5. whom
   6. each other
   7. who
   8. Whose
   9. that/which

E. (Individual writing)

9 The Vancouver Island Marmot

A. 1. mammal ; snout
   2. inhabits
   3. endangered ; extinction
   4. dwindling
   5. ecologically
   6. Research

B. (Individual writing)

C. 1. ✔
   2. ✔
   3. ✗ ; The clear-cut forest resembles the natural habitat of marmots.
   4. ✔
   5. ✗ ; The magazine article explains, "Climate change is already affecting the polar bear population in the Arctic."

D. (Individual writing)

E. (Individual writing)

10 The Governor General's Bravery Awards

A.

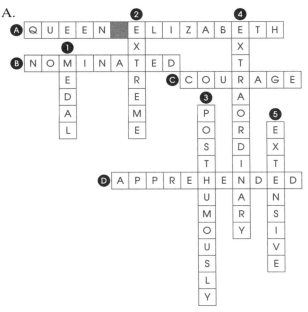

B. 1. ran
2. was cutting ; stormed
3. Did
4. ground
5. was lying ; watched
6. was talking ; struck
7. spread

C. 1. decided
2. went
3. chose
4. brought
5. were skating
6. fell
7. rushed
8. were gasping
9. were losing
10. heard
11. came
12. pulled
13. realized
14. wanted
15. could

11 Necessity Is the Mother of Invention

A. 1. B
2. B
3. C
4. C
5. C

B. (Individual writing)

C. 1. will become
2. will save
3. will be using
4. will be helping
5. will bring

D. 1. "Don't worry," says Kim. "The rain will stop. I know it will."
2. I'm putting this letter on top so that she will read it first.
3. I'm sure Wendy will be staying at home and will be drawing holiday cards for her friends all afternoon.
4. Now that we are able to communicate wirelessly, he will prefer to send me an e-mail instead of a handwritten letter.
5. If you use your diaphragm properly, you will breathe better and will sing better too.
6. When it is colder, the air will clear and the haze will disappear.

E. (Individual writing)

12 He Called Me "Potato Head"!

A.

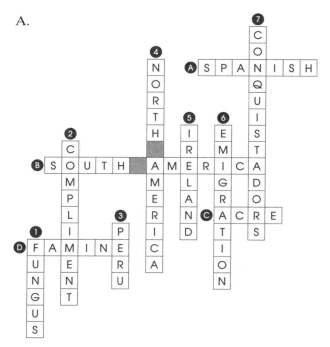

B. 1. dancing ; danced
2. giving ; given
3. spreading ; spread
4. hearing ; heard
5. doing ; done
6. speaking ; spoken
7. rising ; risen
8. choosing ; chosen
9. drawing ; drawn
10. seeing ; seen
11. flying ; flown

C. 1. past participle
2. neither
3. present participle
4. present participle
5. neither
6. past participle

D. 1. ✗   2. ✔
3. ✔   4. ✗
5. ✗

The chuckling grandfather described the goodness of potatoes.

Many people the world over have chosen the potato as their favourite vegetable.

"The fungus has spread to my field as well," a sad farmer said.

13 Asteroids

A. 3 ; 1 ; 5 ; 2 ; 4

B. 1. Hollywood has made great profits from movies depicting the catastrophes resulting from the collisions of asteroids with Earth.
4. The possibility of a Near-Earth Object colliding with Earth is small.
6. The key to protecting Earth is in the finding of the asteroids heading Earth in time to plan a defence strategy.

C. 1. B   2. B
3. B   4. C
5. B   6. A
7. A

D. 1. has become
2. throws
3. did not get
4. changed
5. are

E. (Individual writing)

14 Seven or Eight Summits?

A. 1. archipelago
2. Australasia
3. Mount Everest
4. North America
5. Mount Aconcagua
6. Asia
7. Mount Kosciuszko
8. Pat Morrow

B. (Individual writing)

C. 1. presence
2. than
3. their
4. could've
5. would
6. already
7. loose

D. 1. Whose ; Who's
2. Were ; We're
3. principle ; principal

E. (Individual writing)

F. (Individual writing)

15 The Disappearing Aral Sea

A. 1. Planners in the Soviet Union wanted Central Asia to be the main raw cotton supplier, but this meant that irrigation was necessary, and so the Aral Sea became the source of water.
2. Most of the marshes and wetlands are now sandy deserts, and most of the fish in the Aral Sea, and the wildlife around it, are gone.
3. They are now far away from the seashore. On the rise are incidence of bronchitis, kidney and liver diseases, cancer and arthritic diseases, and high infant mortality rate.
4. (Individual answer)
5. (Individual answer)

B. 1. ✔   2. ✘
3. ✘   4. ✔
5. ✔   6. ✘
7. ✔   8. ✘

Gone are the wildlife around the Aral Sea.
It is a warning sign that the infant mortality rate is at a record high.
"I'll give you a concrete plan once I have it ready," says Gail.
To some people, the president of the U.S. is referred to as "Dubya".

C. Hello everybody. I'm Marmalade. My real name is actually Michelle, but everyone calls me "Marmalade" because I love jam. The nickname somehow stuck. I'm a very messy kid. My mom has told me many, many times to clean up the mess in my room, but I'm always too busy with homework, or too lazy to ever get around to it. There's a sign on my door that says "Marmalade's Room", which I made in my Senior Kindergarten class. Because my room has been in a state of mess for the past six years, my mom teases me all the time. She would ask, "Why don't you make a new sign? 'Marmalade's Mess' would be a pretty cute one, wouldn't it?" To that I'd answer, "There are too many m's in 'Marmalade's Mess'". In any case, my room will never be tidy, so I have all the time in the world to make a new sign. Maybe I'll make one that says "Chaos Within. Watch Your Step." I'll paint the words neon green on black bristol board. Wouldn't that be sharp?

16 All about Salt

A. 1. civil
2. avail
3. preserve
4. mummy
5. soft
6. industry
7. commerce
8. coordinate
9. plenty
10. biology

B. 1. In the old days, Venice's wealth was based on salt.
3. Our bodies need salt for muscle coordination, nerve and heart function, and concentration.
4. Salt enhances flavour and is one of only four tastes the human tongue can distinguish.
5. The Egyptians were the first to make soap with salt.

C. 1. It was freezing this morning; the temperature dropped to -10°C.
2. Our coach told us to take these items with us: a bat, a helmet, and a glove.
3. The package finally arrived: it was the latest video game console.
4. Here is a list of exercises she does in every session: weightlifting, which builds her upper body strength; running, which builds up her endurance; biking, which strengthens her leg muscles.
5. Remember this: when one door closes, another opens.
6. The new company is recruiting the following personnel: a secretary, two sales representatives, and a marketing executive.
7. We tried to stage a comeback; however we couldn't make it in the end.
8. We all overlooked one point: no one actually had all the information.
9. At the party, Joanne met the following people: Miranda, her one-time best friend; Rob, the son of Mrs. Weir, her history teacher; Patricia, her next-door neighbour when she stayed in Peterborough, and Justin, the class clown.

D. 1. The flight (AC068) took 11 hours non-stop to reach the city.
    2. The camp warden told the children to (1) switch off all the lights at ten, (2) get up at seven, and (3) do morning exercise at half past seven.
    3. The seminar (details to be confirmed) will include Dr. John Walsh as one of the speakers.
    4. Samuel Watt (the boy we used to tease) is now a successful business executive.
    5. Members should (a) apply in person, (b) pay a one-time fee of $50, and (c) attend a half-day training course.
    6. Please refer to the map (inset) for the exact route to Bowmanville.
    7. The collection (believed to be donated by the Rodman family) is now on display in the local museum.
    8. The starting pitcher (ERA 3.75) has not lost a game since July 4.
    9. As he is the one handling the complaint (ref. C20-786-03 dated March 23, 2014), you should seek clarification from him.
    10. The graph (see attached) indicates an upward trend between 2011 and 2014.

17 Pauline Johnson

A. 1. E   2. D
    3. A   4. G
    5. H   6. B
    7. C   8. F
B. 1. a. Age in her fingers, hunger in her face,
            Her shoulders stooped with weight of work and years,
            But rich in tawny colouring of her race,
        b. Ere might's injustice banished from their lands
            Her people, that today unheeded lie,
    2. a. Appraised at highest value, cargoes of grain and gold.
        b. Atlantic and far Pacific sweeping her, keel to deck.

C. 1. adverb
    2. adjective
    3. noun
    4. noun
    5. adverb
    6. adjective
    7. adjective
    8. adverb
    9. adjective
    10. adverb
    11. adjective
    12. noun
D. (Individual writing)
E. (Individual writing)

18 Global Climate Change

A. Paragraph One: A
    Paragraph Two: B
    Paragraph Three: C
    Paragraph Four: C
B. 1. ✗
    2. ✗
    3.
    4.
    5. ✗
C. 1. D
    2. D
    3. IND
    4. D
    5. IND
    6. IND
D. (Suggested writing)
    1. The umpire decided to cancel the game because it was raining heavily.
    2. Although he knew his chance of winning was slim, he entered the race nonetheless.
    3. I was walking down the street when I ran into Priscilla's cousin.
    4. Since we are best friends, I have no reason not to help you out again.
    5. Cynthia was on the phone when her parents returned home.
    6. Although Ronald and Tony are twin brothers, they seldom contact each other.
E. (Individual writing)

19 Tina and Grandma's Project

A. (Individual writing)
B. 1. subordinating
   2. coordinating
   3. subordinating
   4. coordinating
   5. subordinating
   6. subordinating
   7. subordinating
   8. coordinating
   9. subordinating
   10. subordinating
C. 2 ; 4 ; 1 ; 3 ; 5
   1. Maria will perform her tune when she feels she can sing it in her sleep.
   2. We need to buy some cookie cutters before we start preparing the dough.
   3. Mom is going to stuff the turkey after she has finished chopping the onions.
   4. Even though Christopher did not make it to the last round of the contest, he remained in good spirit.
   5. Since you have such a good sense of colour, you can help me pick out a dress that looks good on me.

20 Writing

A. 1. Egyptian picture art/communication
   2. phonetic in nature
   3. the ancient Assyrian system of writing
   4. based on sounds
   5. based on pictures or ideas
   6. has 130 000 Chinese characters
   7. people who developed the Western alphabet
B. 1. The earliest attempt was hunting journals found on the walls in caves near Avignon, France.
   2. The western alphabet originated in the Middle East, in the area that is now Lebanon.
   3. It is phonetic, but also incorporates the Chinese writing system.
   4. Phonetic-based languages are easier to learn.
   5. The most important use of writing is communication.

C. 1. CP
   2. CP
   3. CX
   4. CX
   5. CP
   6. CX
D. (Individual writing)
E. (Suggested writing)
   1. Although we did not go to the show, we went skating.
   2. He did not make it in the end even though he tried very hard.
   3. The questions were very tricky so no one could get all of them right.
   4. The swimmers dived in even though the water was freezing.

21 Bear Attack

A. Dos:
   • Back away slowly and cautiously.
   • Watch the bear's reaction.
   • Stop and hold your ground if the bear follows you.
   • Keep a cool head.
   • Drop to the ground if the bear looks like it is going to attack.
   • Curl yourself up into a tight ball and cover your head, chest, and abdomen.

   Don'ts:
   • Do not make eye contact with the bear.
   • Do not panic.
   • Do not turn and run.
   • Do not climb a tree.
   • Do not remove your backpack.
   • Do not struggle or scream.
B. 1.   2. ✔
   3.   4. ✔
   5. ✔   6. ✔
   7.   8. ✔
   9.
C. (Individual writing)

22 A Tree for Boston

A. (Individual writing)
B. 1. A relief train with doctors and desperately needed supplies took off for Nova Scotia
   2. Doctors from Harvard Medical School and the Massachusetts State Guard Medical Unit set up two emergency hospitals.
   3. Non-governmental organizations sent another trainload of clothing, food, money, and medical officers.
   4. A relief concert was held to raise money.
   5. The Massachusetts Automobile Club dispatched a convoy of trucks laden with needed items.
   6. The people of Boston rushed to Boston Harbour to fill a relief boat with supplies.
C. 1. special ; tall ; proud ; prime
   2. Immediately
   3. much-needed
   4. finest
   5. first-ever ; modern
D. (Individual writing)
E. (Individual writing)

23 Charlotte Whitehead Ross

A. 2. Canadian medical schools did not accept women students at the time that Charlotte decided to become a doctor.
   3. Charlotte not only delivered babies but also set broken bones and amputated mangled limbs.
   4. In 1887, Charlotte appealed to the Manitoba Legislature to grant her a licence but they refused.
B. (Individual writing)

C. Michaelle Jean was born in Haiti in 1957. At the age of ten, she and her family fled the dictator regime in Haiti to settle in Quebec, Canada. She studied language and literature at the University of Montreal and, from 1984 to 1986, taught Italian Studies while completing a Master of Arts degree in comparative literature. Not long after her studies, Michaelle helped establish a network of shelters for women and children across the country, and worked in organizations that helped new immigrants. When Radio-Canada hired her in 1988, Michaelle started working as a reporter, later becoming the host of programs such as *The Passionate Eye* and *Rough Cuts*, which broadcast the best Canadian and foreign documentary films. By 2004, she began her own show, *Michaelle*, while continuing as host for other programs. In 2005, Michaelle was appointed Governor General, becoming the first black woman to represent the Queen for Canada.
D. (Individual writing)

24 Politics in Canada

A. 1. Conservative Party
      Liberal Party
      New Democratic Party
      Green Party
      Bloc Québécois
   2. MPs: Members of Parliament
      MLAs: Members of the Legislative Assembly
      MHAs: Members of the House of Assembly
      MNAs: Members of the National Assembly
      MPPs: Members of the Provincial Parliament
B. 1. ✘   2. ✔
   3. ✔   4. ✘
   5. ✔   6. ✘
   7. ✘   8. ✘
   9. ✔
C. (Individual writing)
D. (Individual writing)

25 Pierre Laporte

A. 1 ; 6 ; 2 ; 3 ; 5 ; 4
B. (Individual writing)
C. 1. Someone turned off the lights in the library and Adrian does not know who did it.
   2. Adrian does not know who turned off the lights. He calls for help but no one answers and he tries to find the exit but he cannot see in the dark.
   3. Adrian needs to find the exit before he gets locked inside the library for the whole weekend.
D. (Individual writing)

26 Urbanization

A. (Individual writing)
B. (Individual writing)
C. 1.
   2.
   3. ✔
   4.
   5. ✔
D. (Individual answers)
E. (Individual writing)

27 Waltzing Matilda

A. 1. F   2. T
   3. F   4. T
   5. F   6. T
B. (Individual writing)
D. 1. Mood:
      serious
      Technique:
      sensory detail (sight) ; Three policemen came.
   2. Mood:
      sad
      Technique:
      sensory detail (sound) ; The ghost of the swagman can be heard as he sings.
E. (Individual writing)

28 New School, New Life

A. (Individual writing)
B. 1. light-hearted ; bright
   2. grey ; sad
C. (Individual writing)

1 The Founding Nations of Canada

A. 1. natural
2. Catholic
3. individual
4. societal
5. British
6. parliament
7. Indigenous Peoples
8. colonies

B. The First Peoples:
A, D, E, H, I
(Individual example)
The French:
C, G
(Individual example)
The British:
B, C, F, J, K
(Individual example)
(Individual answer)

2 Immigration to Canada

A. 1. land
2. colonies
3. slavery
4. freedom
5. farming
6. food
7. famine
8. poverty
9. diseases
10. job
11. wars

B. E
H
F
C
D
A
G
I
B
(Individual answer)

3 Home Children in Canada

A. 1. orphaned   2. labour
3. domestic   4. adopted
5. exploited   6. farms
7. 2010   8. descendants

B. (Individual answers)

4 The Chinese Canadians

A. B ; E ; F ; C ; D ; A
The Chinese immigrants in Canada could not afford to bring their families to Canada and had to live separately from them.

B. 1. sacrifices   2. trade
3. patriotism   4. businesses
5. invest   6. economic
7. ethic   8. community

5 The Japanese Canadians

A. 1. B   2. C
3. E   4. A
5. D

B.

(Individual answer)

6 The Demolition of Africville

A. 1. Black Loyalists
2. Halifax
3. utilities
4. undesirable
5. dump
6. renewal
7. industrial
8. church
9. protests
10. apologized
11. replica

B.

(Individual answer)

7 The Image of Canada

A. hockey
Canadian flag
beaver
maple leaf
lacrosse
grain elevator
Parliament Buildings
1. lacrosse
2. Parliament Buildings
3. Canadian flag
4. beaver
5. grain elevator
6. Canadian horse
B. (Individual answers)

8 Multiculturalism in Canada

A.

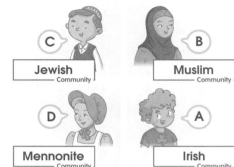

B. 1. ethnic
2. religious
3. military
4. Waterloo
5. technology
6. buggies
Old Order Mennonite Community
Religion: Christianity
Clothing: plain and simple
Use of Technology: avoid using modern technology
Means of Transport: horses and buggies
Education: schools run by Mennonite community
My Community
(Individual answers)

9 Ethnic Neighbourhoods

A. majority ; language ; growth ; major ; restaurants ; traditional
B. (Suggested answers)
New Immigrants: A ; B ; D ; G ; H
Some Established Canadians: C ; E ; F ; I

10 Support and Inclusiveness

A. 1. advocacy organizations for immigrants ; rights ; influence ; refugees ; society
2. labour organizations ; workers ; bargaining ; equality ; workforce
B. (Suggested answers)
1. People with intellectual disabilities feel at home with L'Arche's support assistants in these environments.

2. It is important for developing mutual respect and for representing an inclusive society.
3. (Individual answer)

11 Human Rights and Violations

A.

Canadian Human Rights Act	Ontario Human Rights Code
✓	✓
✓	✓
✓	✓
✓	✓
✓	✓
○	✓
✓	✓
○	✓
✓	✓
○	✓
✓	○

(Suggested answer)
The Canadian Human Rights Act protects federal employees and people receiving services from the federal government, the First Nations governments, and federal government-regulated companies; the Ontario Human Rights Code protects people in Ontario.

B. 1. He should turn to the Ontario Human Rights Code for protection.
2. Aadil was discriminated against based on the grounds of race and creed.

12 Income Inequality

A. 1. New immigrants, visible minorities, women, and people with lower levels of education are negatively affected.
2-4. (Individual answers)
B. Social Differences: B, C, D, E, G
Economic Differences: A, F

13 Canada's Free Trade Agreements

A. 1. services   2. tariffs
3. quotas   4. competitive

B. with Israel
with Peru
with Colombia
with Jordan
with Panama
1. Canada-U.S. Free Trade Agreement
2. North American Free Trade Agreement
(Suggested answers)
3. This is because the U.S. and Mexico are geographically close to Canada so transporting goods is convenient.
4. All of Canada's trading partners are countries in the West and most have access to large bodies of water.

14 Canada and the United Nations

A. 1. peace
   2. cooperation
   3. human rights
   4. objectives
   MDGs

 poverty   education

 equality   mortality

 maternal

B.

(Individual answer and drawing)

15 Children's Rights

A. 1. name   2. parents
   3. harm   4. opinion
   5. medical   6. government
   7. education   8. culture
   9. play
B. 1. Yes, it is reflected in a child's right to receive an education in English or French.
   2. There are more criminal laws to prevent child abuse and the maximum punishments for those who violate these laws have been greatly increased.
   3. Ontario addresses children's rights to be protected from work that harms them.

16 The World Health Organization

A. A ; B ; D ; E ; F ; G
B. 1. (Suggested answer)
   Canada participates in WHO with other countries in the world to reduce various fatal diseases.
   2. It shows that foreign-born Canadians were the most susceptible to TB.
   3. Participating in WHO allows Canada to work with the rest of the world in combating TB, which is also a challenging issue in Canada.
   4. (Individual answer)

17 The Kyoto Protocol

A. 1. international   2. Japan
   3. 2005   4. legally
   5. carbon dioxide   6. 1998
   7. 6%   8. climate
   9. reducing
B. 1. The Kyoto Protocol is an international agreement under the UNFCCC. Its main purpose is to reduce six greenhouse gases.
   2. Canada's greenhouse gas emissions since 1990 have been much higher than the Kyoto target.
   3. Canada has committed to reducing greenhouse gas emissions under the Copenhagen Accord.

18 Non-governmental Organizations

A. non-profit ; citizens ; humanitarian
   medical ; doctors ; public ; Peace ; impartiality ; medical
B. 1. medical
   2. diseases
   3. hygiene
   4. centres
   5. food
   6. officers
   7. managing
   8. improve
C. 1. 1991
   2. (Any three) Colombia, Haiti, Ivory Coast, Nigeria, Papua New Guinea, the Republic of the Congo

19 Free The Children

A. Founders: Craig Kielburger and 11 of his classmates
Year Founded: 1995
Goals:
- to free children from poverty and exploitation
- to free young people from the thought that they cannot do anything to bring positive changes to the world

B.

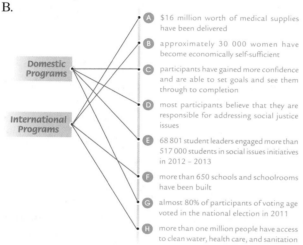

C. (Individual writing)

20 Canada's International Aid

A. 1. needs
2. foreign
3. nutrition
4. agricultural
5. education
6. maternal
7. businesses
8. training
B. Top 10 Recipients:
1. Tanzania
2. Ethiopia
3. Congo
4. Côte d'Ivoire
5. Ghana
6. Haiti
7. Afghanistan
8. Bangladesh
9. Mali
10. Mozambique
1. Africa
2. seven countries
3. (Individual answer)

21 The 2010 Haiti Earthquake

A. 1. earthquake
2. aftershocks
3. infrastructure
4. communication
5. humanitarian
6. security
7. evacuated
8. donations
9. debt

B.

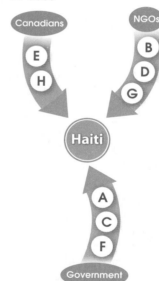

22 SARS in Canada

A. 1. Toronto   2. provincial
   3. precautions   4. health
   5. health care   6. respirators
   7. hospitals   8. emergency
   9. over

B. 1. (Individual answer)
   2. (Individual answer)
   3. Quarantine is necessary to contain the outbreak and prevent the spread of an infectious disease.
   4. SARS is an airborne disease. Mia wore a mask to avoid spreading the disease to her mom.

B. 1. (Individual answer)
   2. United Kingdom and France
   3. (Individual answer)

23 Invasive Species in Canada

Zebra Mussel: unintentional
Emerald Ash Borer: unintentional
Common Buckthorn: intentional
Emerald Ash Borer ; C
Zebra Mussel ; B
Common Buckthorn ; A
(Individual answer)

24 Canada's Tourist Sources and Destinations

A. Top 6 countries visited by Canadians (2012):
   1. United States
   2. Mexico
   3. Cuba
   4. United Kingdom
   5. Dominican Republic
   6. France

Top 6 countries tourists to Canada came from (2012):
(Suggested answers)
   1. 39° N   112° W
   2. 53° N   1° W
   3. 49° N   2° E
   4. 53° N   13° E
   5. 30° N   110° E
   6. 26° S   129° E

1 Classification of Living Things (1)

A. Living: B, D, E, G, I
   Non-living: A, C, F, H, J

   Plant: D, G, I
   Animal: B, E
   Rubber: C, F
   Metal: A, H, J

B. Check the letters: B, D, E, F, G, H
   Cross out the letters: A, C

C. 1. monera
   2. fungi
   3. animals
   4. plants
   5. protists

2 Classification of Living Things (2)

A. 1. Kingdom
      Phylum
      Class
      Order
      Family
      Genus
      Species
   2. kingdom
   3. kingdom, phylum, class, order, and family

B. Housefly: Musca domestica
   Grey wolf: Canis lupus
   Chimpanzee: Pan troglodytes

C. 1.

      reason: no backbone
   2.

      reason: not in the cat family
   3.

      reason: cannot make food

3 Invertebrates

A.

B. Porifera: sponges ; A
   Coelenterata: jellyfish ; D
   Arthropoda: insects ; E
   Mollusca: snails ; F
   Echinodermata: starfish ; C
   Annelida: segmented worms ; B

4 Arthropods

A. 1. B
   2. D
   3. E
   4. A
   5. C

B. Class: Crustacea
   Class: Insecta ; 3
   Class: Arachnida ; 4 ; 0
   Class: Myriapoda ; many ; 1

C. 1. thorax
   2. wings
   3. exoskeleton

5 Vertebrates

A. 1. true
   2. false

3. true
4. false
5. false
6. true
7. true

B. 1. Fish ;

2. Amphibians ;

3. Mammals ;

4. Birds ;

5. Reptiles ;

C. 1. a. fish ; mammal
   b. fish ; mammal
   c. mammal ; fish
2. a. reptile ; amphibian
   b. bird ; reptile

6 Vertebrate Adaptations

A. reptile eggs: D
   amphibian lungs: F
   bird beaks: A
   mammary glands: C
   bird bones: B
   the teeth of mammals: E
B. 1. endothermic ; constant
   2. exothermic ; overheating
   3. warm ; cold
   4. insulator

7 Air

A. 1. mass
   2. gravity
   3. weight
   4. a.

b.

B. 1. has weight
   2. takes up space
   3. expands when
      heated

Experiment (Individual observation)
The air is providing the extra weight.

8 Bernoulli's Principle

A. 1. less
   2. lower
   3. higher
B. 1. low
   2. High
   3. lift
C.

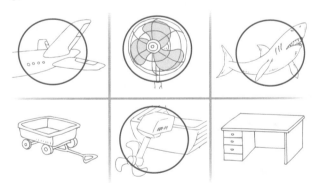

D. (Suggested drawings)
   bike helmet:

   toy car:

9 Flight (1)

A. 1.

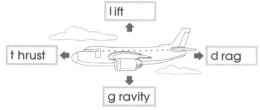

2. drag
3. lift
4. thrust
5. gravity

B. 1. engine ; thrust
   2. hot air ; lift

C.

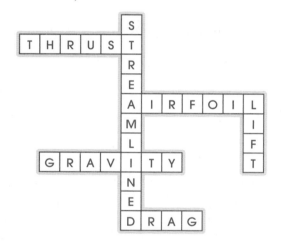

10 Flight (2)

A. rocket: D
   glider: F
   hot-air balloon: A
   airplane: H
   paper airplane: B
   helicopter: G
   kite: C
   parachute: E

B. 1. parachute ; dandelion seeds
   2. helicopter ; maple seeds
   3. airplane ; bird

C. (Suggested answers)
   helium balloon, bee, space shuttle, firefly, jet plane, blimp

11 History of Air and Space Travel

A. 1. A
   2. A
   3. B
   4. A

B.

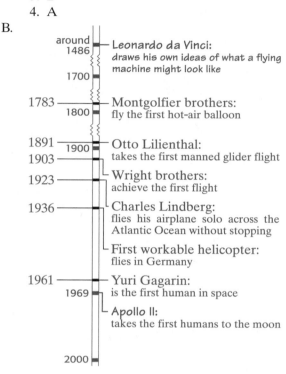

12 Static and Current Electricity

A. 1. Static
   2. Current

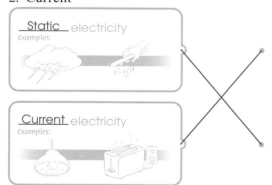

B. 1. electrons ; negative ; positive
2. a.

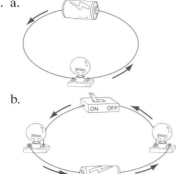

b.

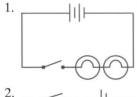

Experiment (Individual observation)

13 Circuits

A. 1. light bulb
2. wire
3. switch
4. battery
B. 1. B
2. A
3. C
C. 1.

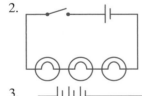

2.

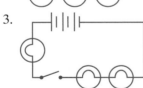

3.

4.

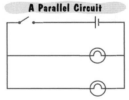

14 Conductors and Insulators

A. Colour the light bulbs in pictures 1 and 4.
B. 1.

2.

3.

C. 1. an insulator
2. conducts
3. conductor
4. a conductor

15 Electricity

A. 1. Series ; Parallel
2. series
3. parallel
4. parallel
5. series

B.

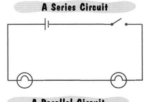

C.

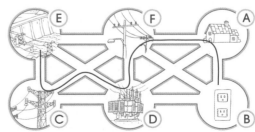

16 Sources of Electricity

A. 1. wind
   2. tides
   3. battery
   4. Geothermal
   5. moving water
   6. Nuclear
   7. oil ; gas ; coal
   8. solar
B. 1. 42 576 ; 45 832 ; 3256
   2. 23 914 ; 28 471 ; 4557
   3. B

17 Motion

A.

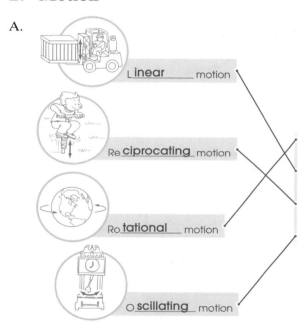

L__inear__ motion

Re__ciprocating__ motion

Ro__tational__ motion

O__scillating__ motion

B. 1. reciprocating
   2. A: rotational
       B: linear
   3. oscillating
Try this: (Suggested answer)
A merry-go-round can show rotational motion as a whole and reciprocating motion with its horses.
You can tap your head with your left hand to show reciprocating motion and rub your tummy in a circular motion with your right hand to show rotational motion.

18 Friction

A. 1. B
   2. A
   3. B
B. 1. ball bearings ; decrease ; greater ; lesser
   2. chalk ; increase
   3. increases ; reduced ; oil

19 Movement and Levers

A. 1. effort, load ;

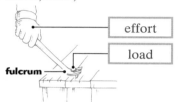

   2. effort, fulcrum ;

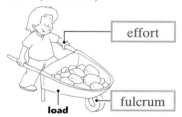

   3. load, fulcrum ;

B. 1. increases
   2. load ; effort force
   3. does not increase ; less ; increases
C. 1. 2nd
   2. 1st
   3. 3rd

20 Solar System

A.
1. false
2. true
3. true
4. true
5. true
6. false
7. false

B. comet ; D
moon ; A
meteoroids ; E
aurora borealis ; C
planet ; B

21 The Moon

A.

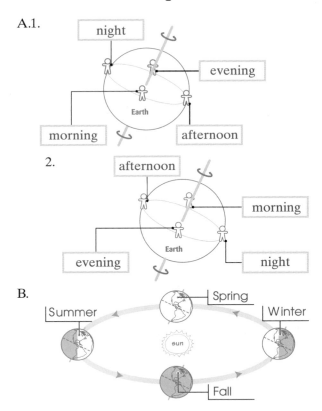

B. Maria ; Meteorites ; craters
The Moon:
1. maria
2. crater
3. crater
4. maria
5. maria
6. crater

22 Constellations

A.
1. Ursa Minor ; A
2. Ursa Major ; C
3. Cassiopeia ; D
4. Cepheus ; B
5. Draco ; E

B.

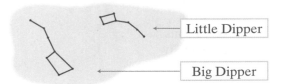

Little Dipper

Big Dipper

23 The Earth in Space

A.1.

night
evening
morning
afternoon
Earth

2.

afternoon
morning
evening
night
Earth

B.

Spring
Summer
Winter
sun
Fall

Experiment (Individual observation)

24 Humans in Space

A. 1. low
    2. equator
    3. faster
    4. higher
B. 1. orbit
    2. Space shuttles
    3. astronauts
    4. experiments
    5. microgravity
    6. muscles
    7. countries
    8. The home in space is the International Space Station.
    9. Many different countries of the world are involved in the project.